Tomorrow,

Tina Johnston

GreenSunsetBooks

www.greensunsetbooks.co.uk

First published in 2009 by
Green Sunset Books
92 Mosse Gardens, Fishbourne
PO19 3PQ
www.greensunsetbooks.co.uk

Cover image: © 2009 Tina Smart
Line Drawings: © 2009 Tina Smart
Cover design and page layout by Adrian Floyde
www.pure-survival.com

A catalogue record for this book is available from the
British Library

For my two children
Annabelle and Nicolas
(in no particular order)

For the Moroccan people, especially my friends out there

Thanks...

... to everyone who encouraged me to keep writing. In English. I love the language.

... to Stephanie Norgate, Dave Swann, Jane Rusbridge, Alison MacLeod, Stephen Mollet, Karen Stevens, Hugh Dunkerly – my MA tutors at the University of Chichester, for teaching me how to write.

... to my neighbours in Morocco. They are my family, and I miss them when I am not out there.

...to Adrian, who keeps converting my numerous files into pdf without complaining, and who assembled the cover of this book.

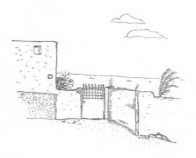

Chapter One

The roadside café was a breezy and spacious place. The tables and chairs on the terrace were shaded by cascades of vine pouring down from a metal canopy.

The owner of the café looked up from his newspaper. He was uncommonly beefy and unshaven.

"*Bonjour, Monsieur*," I said cheerfully.

He grunted in response.

I ordered a coffee, sat down under the vine and spread a map across the table. I was the only customer. Still, I waited for a long time.

Finally, the sound of sandals being dragged across the stone floor announced the owner's approach. He set a glass of milky coffee in front of me with ferocity; the light brown liquid spilled over my map. I watched Morocco disappear in a muddy flood.

"*Shokran*," I said, but he had already turned and was shuffling back. I felt as welcome as an uninvited guest at a dinner party, so I drained what was left in my glass and went inside to pay.

"*Dix-huit dirham.*" He glinted down at me from his towering position behind the counter, where he was polishing a glass.

Eighteen *dirham*! I clenched my fists. 'You might look big and strong and intimidating,' I thought, 'but I will not let you get away with it.'

"*Monsieur*, this is neither my first time in Morocco nor my first visit to a café in this country. I am aware that in some cafés tourists are charged more money than local people, but your price for a glass of coffee is outrageous and insulting. I am going to pay you ten dirham, which is still two dirham more than it should be," I said in my best French, wondering what possessed me to take on a giant like this.

The giant dropped the tea towel and slowly walked around the counter. He stopped in front of me, his hands on his hips, and stared. I felt myself turn red and wished I could unsay what I had said.

Unexpectedly, he burst into laughter. He grabbed my hand and shook it, almost dislocating my shoulder.

"You no pay," he said in English, still laughing.

"Oh yes, I insist on giving you ten dirham." I put a coin on the counter.

When I drove off, he was standing in the doorway of his café, waving good-bye with one hand and still wiping tears of laughter from his eyes with the other.

Unpredictable and full of surprises, I thought on my way to Taghazout, that's what I loved about this country.

Chapter Two

A film of moisture covered my skin. My cotton dress tried to
stick to my body like cling film. My mouth was dry, and my
heart was still beating fast from the unusual strain. Salim, who
had the weathered wrinkled face of a seventy-year old fisherman,
without being either one or the other, looked as fresh as he had
back down in Taghazout.

Below, the sandy coast stretched south, past Agadir, until
the golden strip grew thinner and hazier. Finally, it disappeared
on its long way around the African continent. Villages perched
almost invisibly on the surrounding hilltops, the flat-roofed,
earth coloured mud huts blending harmoniously into the
countryside. The slim tower of the mosque, whitewashed with a
green tiled roof, stood erect and proud like a soldier on guard. To
the east, the countryside was barren and hilly, rising and falling
and rising again, higher and higher, from hills to mountains and
finally to heights of thousands of metres: the High Atlas. To the
west, there was the Atlantic Ocean, roaring faintly and
displaying spectacular sunsets every evening.

Each time I came up here, it seemed more beautiful.

Salim was pacing up and down, dirty feet clinging on to
broken sandals, thin dusty legs sticking out of a brown, torn
djellaba.

"*Madame, azih!*" he pleaded, mopping his balding skull with his sleeve and rearranging his crocheted *Kufi* cap.

Only a few sounds drifted through the village. I heard the bleating of sheep and goats, the occasional braying of donkeys and the melodious chatter of the village women. From a classroom somewhere, children were reading out of the *Koran*. The chanting of their clear voices danced through the dusty streets. There was a muffled thunder, like a subterranean explosion, every time the ocean waves crashed against the rocky shore far below.

It was peaceful. It was warm. The air smelled of wood fire. Salim stepped forward and pulled my sleeve.

"*Madame, shuf!*"

He pointed at an unfinished grey breezeblock building on the edge of the village. It was facing south and measured about sixty square metres. Years ago, in a half-hearted attempt to create a house, Salim had built four breezeblock walls onto the boundaries of the land. The breezeblocks had been laid in a rolling fashion as if by a drunken bricklayer. The walls leant against each other for support. The building looked like a decaying roofless air-raid shelter.

"*Azih, Madam!*" Salim hurried to unlock a rusty metal door in one of the walls.

I followed him inside. I had never seen a building as uninspiring as this one. The floor was no more than a rectangle of rocky hill surface trapped within four rickety walls. Near the door, it sported a small concrete square.

"*Eau potable.*" Salim knew the odd French words, which enabled us to exchange at least a minimum of information. He lifted the concrete square which turned out to be the entrance to a cistern: a dark and dank cavern, emanating the odour of stale water and old cellars.

Most of the floor was covered by the remnants of Salim's building work. Breezeblocks and sand were piled up into an untidy mound. Salamanders dashed in and out of the porous bricks. A purple geranium grew in solitude behind a heap of gravel. It was the only flower I had seen so far in Taliouine, probably because the goats could not reach it. If the flower could make a living in such a harsh environment – why should I not be able to?

I stepped back out through the metal door and straight into the view along the coast. My eyes travelled south, and I lost myself in the distance.

"*Madame?*" Salim had followed me, playing with the keys. He had no time for views or contemplations. His need was basic and urgent. He wanted to sell his land and preferably today. I wished he would leave me alone for a while.

Two women approached. They were dressed in colourful clothes, leggings-clad legs hidden under long skirts. Cheap plastic sandals were holding beautifully hennaed feet like exquisite paintings carelessly stuffed into shoddy frames. The women's dark hair was just about covered by brightly patterned headscarves.

"*La bes,*" the older woman said, unsmilingly.

"*La bes, bejer?*" I returned her greeting.

The young woman giggled. The older one twisted her mouth into a smile. For a split second, a silvery tooth reflected the sunlight.

It was not the warmest of welcomes. Would the village people accept me, even like me? Or was I too different? I had taken to dressing very traditionally in Morocco as not to offend anybody. My dresses had mostly long sleeves, were rather shapeless and I, too, wore leggings underneath. But was it enough? What if they avoided or excluded me, considering my settling amongst them an intrusion? We did not have a language in common. I spoke neither Berber nor Arabic, and the mountain world did not understand French.

I should buy land in France or Italy, as other people did. Why did it have to be Morocco? A country, where culture and language were so different to mine?

The answer was easy. It had to be Morocco, because I loved it. I felt almost at home. I was tired of travelling, of being uprooted. I had recovered from the pain of the past. The friendliness and hospitality of the Moroccan people had helped to restore my faith. I wanted to be part of a community, a family, have neighbours and friends. I was ready to live amongst people again. I felt no desire to return to Europe though, to the loneliness of the so-called western civilisation.

There was no electricity and no running water up in Taliouine. I did not mind. I had managed without it for seven years now and found it an economical and rewarding way to live. Every house in the village had a cistern. A lorry delivered fresh water from Tamraght, a nearby riverside village. And as far as electricity was concerned - people here lived a far more natural life. They went to sleep when it grew dark and got up with the first light in the morning. If light was needed after sunset, fires, gas lamps or candles were lit.

This part of the country was amazingly untouched by tourism and development, although it was only fifteen kilometres north of Agadir and sported five kilometres of unspoilt beach. I dreaded the day the tourism industry would develop the area. I could envisage a hotel resort, complete with golf course and artificial marina, taking over the fields and the beach. It would be a nightmare, but as everything in this country takes a long time to materialise, I was hopeful that any development would not start within the next decade. There was talk of bringing electricity up to the mountain world, *insha'allah,* which I did not look forward to either, because I wanted to be green and go back to nature. Usually one could rely on *"insha'allah",* meaning that nothing would happen if Allah did not approve of it, and in my experience, Allah takes his time to make decision.

"Sir, sir!" Salim hissed, flicking a bony hand at the women. They moved into the shadow of a house.

"Madame, Taghazout," Salim pressed to walk back. He pointed at the sun, which was almost setting. Carefully, he locked the rusty door which seemed to be holding the four walls together.

"Beslama," I said to the women.

The old woman nodded but did not return my farewell. The younger women giggled once more, then put her hand over her mouth. Two sets of dark eyes burned holes into my back until I was out of sight.

Taghazout is an old fishing village, cut into two communities by the coast road to Casablanca: the *commune maritime* by the sea and the *commune rurale* on the hillside. The dwellings spreading down towards the sea were the oldest in the village. Mostly made from mud and stones, they leant this way and that way and thus stopped each other from tumbling down the steep slopes into the ocean. The whitewashed walls were brightened by ornate and vividly coloured metal doors, through which visitors stepped into traditional courtyards. The seafront was lined with "done-up" houses, former fishermen's dwellings, inhabited infrequently by Europeans or Americans.

Although there were many tourists and plenty of non-Moroccans, who had settled here more or less permanently, Taghazout had not lost much of its medievalness. The only recent modernisation was the arrival of electricity about twenty years ago and, even more recent, running water, but certainly not available in every house. The paths running down to the beach were dusty and covered with litter: paper, chicken bones, vegetable peels.

On the other side of the road, buildings crawled up the hillside. These more recent buildings were made from breezeblocks and cement. Some were plastered and painted, but most of them were grey and bare like Salim's four walls. The dry mud paths were steep and strewn with rubbish and building debris. A bumpy track made its almost vertical way up the back of the village until it picked up the newly surfaced road into the hills.

The sides of the main road were lined with cafés, providing local food and soft drinks to the male population of Taghazout. The only women found in the cafés were foreigners.

My friend Yassin owned one of the cafés.

I climbed up the four uneven cement steps to the terrace of Yassin's café and slumped onto one of the faded orange plastic

13

chairs. The smell of rotting waste wafted across from the dried out river bed where it had been dumped by the villagers. Every spring, when the snow on the peaks of the High Atlas melts, the river fills with water and carries the decomposing waste off to the sea. For the rest of the year it was left to rot. On hot days, the stench was suffocating.

The terrace was covered with bamboo and sported a few naked light bulbs. A limp looking vine seemed reluctant to grow any further than half way up the corner post.

Yassin appeared at my table and put a steaming *tajine* in front of me, the traditional Moroccan stew, which had been simmering on a charcoal stove for hours. Potatoes and vegetables were still sizzling in the oil. A scent of coriander and cumin emanated from the dish.

"I told you about bandits," he said sternly. "You must not walk down alone after dark." He put the basket with freshly baked bread down rather firmly.

"Yes, Yassin, yes," I answered, took a flat round bread and tore a piece off. "It is not dark yet, by the way. And I was with Salim."

Yassin ignored the remark and helped himself to a bottle from the glass fridge, which displayed an assortment of soft drinks made by an American company. The cooling system had broken down long ago.

He pulled a chair from the next table. He turned it round, straddled it and rested his arms on the back.

"Come on, tell me - what you think?" he said, forever stumbling through the minefield of English grammar.

I scooped up some of the *tajine* with my bread. For a while, I considered the Moroccan habit of using bread and fingers instead of knives, forks or spoons. It was definitely much more fun to eat like that. It also saved the washing up. And the expense of having to buy cutlery. What a strange thing civilisation was!

Yassin's impatient voice woke me out of my musings.

"You like it?"

"Do I like it?" I sighed, stuffing a saffron coloured potato into my mouth. "Yassin, I love it."

Yassin was the mediator, the estate agent between Salim and me. Not only out of friendship to me - I had no illusions about it - but also for a juicy commission from Salim.

I looked at him. He was wearing his favourite t-shirt, brought from Europe as a present by a customer. It was light blue and sported the label of an English sportswear manufacturer as well as a large number six and the name of a German football team. Yassin loved labels almost as much as he loved football and had a collection of designer wear, presented to him by his large number of international friends on their visits to Taghazout. I have never seen him wear the Moroccan *djellaba*, the traditional hooded ankle-length overcoat. He was a slim man, only half a head taller than I was. We were born in the same months of the same year, maybe even on the same day, but there was no concrete information on Yassin's side.

"Yassin, you are my friend, aren't you?"

"Of course." Yassin shifted around on his chair. Personal conversations involving his feelings embarrassed him most of the time. He was a man of action, not words.

"Do you think I should leave it? Is it a silly idea? Building a house in an Arabic country? Not understanding the language? Being a woman? Would it not be better, if I just rented something when I came here?"

Yassin considered it for a short while. He folded his arms across his chest and said in his best English: "No, renting is no good for you. You need a home. You want a house – you build a house. You have friends here. Friends will help you. You are a woman. So what? Women are more free in Morocco now." After this uncharacteristically long speech, he got up. "And you are not a Moroccan woman." He disappeared into his small café and took refuge behind his counter.

I watched him fondly. Yassin had been my friend for many years and I trusted his judgement. When I entered his café for the first time in search of cooked food, he had been standing behind the counter as he was now. I liked his slightly cheeky smile, which reached every corner of his face, his friendliness and his unusual blue eyes. Although he said that some Berbers have blue eyes I have never seen one. Yassin and I have always been good friends. Not once did I see him as a potential lover in all those years, although I have to admit that his eyes could stir something inside me if I allowed it. However, I was still too much affected by the past to consider anything other than friendship. Over the years we built up a relationship, which appeared deep and unconditional and bore the possibility of taking it a step further, but neither he nor I have so far attempted to explore beyond the borders, too frightened to challenge the fundaments of our friendship.

Yassin looked up, caught my eyes and put up his thumb. I grinned and turned my attention back to my *tajine*. I picked the last bits of cumin-spiced chicken meat off the stick-like bones and wiped and scooped the coriander-infused sauce until the dish was bone dry.

Around me, the nightlife of Taghazout was unfolding. The male population had returned from their dwellings and their evening meals. Men in dark *djellabas* clustered together in small groups, shadowy figures in the paleness of dim streetlights. Sitting on walls, in cafés, on the pavement, they were talking, gambling, smoking, even trading. The odd European couple moved up and down the village, clutching each other's hands and scanning the menus outside the cafés. I heard Berber music from a stall opposite, a rhythmic teamwork of *darabouka* drums, metallic *qraqebs* and *rababs*, the one-stringed fiddle.

Unintelligible bits of conversation drifted through the air which was warm and smelled of glowing charcoal and fried fish. Taghazout's stalls and cafes were lit up by naked light bulbs dangling down from the ceilings by cables, with clouds of flies forming amorphous lampshades around them.

The loudspeakers mounted on the tower of the mosque came to life with a scratching noise. The music in the street was turned off. Conversations ceased. The village fell silent. For a while, only the tinny voice of the *mu'adh-dhin* could be heard praising Allah and inviting the faithful to prayer, the *adhan*.

After the call, conversations were resumed and the music started up again.

Yassin brought two glasses of mint tea.

"Look at the French," he grumbled, glaring at the neighbouring café. It was crammed with people. Not like Yassin's café which at that moment was only hosting an envious landlord and a crazy woman from England. While Yassin's clientele was local and poor, the "French" - so named because the café was run by French ex-pats - were entertaining tourists, surfers and rich Moroccans. The French café, its real name unsuitably being "Copacabana", was in fashion. There were candles on the table and the waiters served food on plates, with cutlery and yellow napkins. European music and carefree conversations floated through the air.

"We must do something about it, Yassin. Maybe redecorate your café? What do you think?"

It was not Yassin's favourite subject. He got up and collected our glasses.

"You must go and think about the house. You come for lunch tomorrow."

I pushed my chair back.

"*Beslama*, Yassin."

I bounced down the steps into the street. Yes, I should buy the land, build a house and make a home here. And if there were going to be a few obstacles I would overcome them. It should not be anything major. I hoped.

Chapter Three

With the warmth of the sun on my back and the expanse of the
High Atlas in front of me, I clambered up the steep hillside again
the next day. The sweet smell of stables hung in the air, heavy
like a thick blanket. A woman's high-pitched voice trailed across
from a small farm, her Berber staccato piercing the air. The
mosque on the distant hilltop crackled to life. *Allah Akbar*! A
tinny voice was calling the mountain world to prayer. Wood fires
had been going since dawn, filling the air with a promise of fresh
bread and *tajine*. Nothing moved except for some goats high up
in the Argan trees, balancing on tiny hoofs along spiky branches
eating every Argan nut in their way.

There was little vegetation on the hills behind Taghazout.
The ground was stony and dry, barren yet striking in its different
shades of brown. Fertility was only evident in the small,
cultivated fields I passed. Uneven walls made from piled up
stones surrounded the carpets of pale green shoots and were
topped with the prickly branches of the Argan tree, to keep
unwelcome intruders out.

I climbed on, straight up the hill, picking up here and there
a well-trodden path, until I reached the dusty track, the
Moroccan equivalent of an access road, leading up to the village
of Taliouine. The surface consisted of dried mud, stones and
large potholes, and I wondered if it was at all possible to bring

my van up here. I followed the track which zigzagged its way up the hill, past two or three low dwellings. Finally, I arrived at Said's piece of land with its four uneven walls.

It could be mine.

I felt a pang of excitement.

"*La bes, Madame*," a voice said behind me.

I turned round. It was the same woman as yesterday. I guessed that she was about sixty years old, but knowing how early people aged in Morocco, she was probably only in her forties. She was tall for a Moroccan woman, with a hard pinched face and a turned-down mouth.

"*La bes, Madame, bejer*?" I greeted.

She smiled hesitantly. A young woman stepped out of a green door in a white washed wall, bouncing a small child on her hip. She paused for a second, then came slowly towards us.

"Nashiema!" The old woman pointed at the younger one.

Nashiema's face was finely drawn. Her large eyes were dark and almond shaped, and her nose was straight and small. Her lips curved into a shy warm smile. I could see that Nashiema was her daughter, a friendlier and more beautiful version of the older woman.

"Cherifa!" the older woman said, pointing at herself.

"Kate." I introduced myself.

"Kett. Kett." They giggled, shook their heads and discarded my unfamiliar sounding name like an uncomfortable shoe.

"*Madame*." Cherifa decided.

I hoped she was not being serious. If I were going to be *Madame* I would always be the odd one out in the village. Being called *Madame* stressed the enormous difference between us, my culture and their culture, unless I also called them *Madame*.

"*Madame* Cherifa. *Madame* Nashiema," I tried.

Cherifa and Nashiema bent over laughing.

"*Oho*," Cherifa said, waggling her index finger vigorously. "Cherifa. Nashiema. *Mezyan*!"

My dream of being one with the villagers was moving into the distance.

"*Madame*!"

20

Cherifa as possibly the village eldest had made her decision. I had no choice but to get used to my new name.

"*Madame, atei!*"

I was a foreigner. I sighed.

"*Azih, Madame, atei!*" Cherifa's impatient voice rang through to me.

Atei? I looked up. She was pointing at the green door. I was invited for tea in Cherifa's house. I watched her turn and walk up the path, slipping on small rocks in her torn plastic sandals.

"*Azih!*" she shouted without turning round.

"*Azih!*" Nashiema repeated and hooked her arm through mine. A sweet scent of flowers and spices emanated from her hair.

We followed her mother. I felt a tiny pat on my shoulder. When I turned my head, I looked straight into a pair of almost black eyes and a beaming smile.

"Samir." Nashiema introduced her baby to me, who was strapped around her hip with a piece of brightly coloured material.

Samir leant across Nashiema, his eager little face framed by a thicket of black curls bouncing like tiny springs. A starfish-shaped hand was trying to get hold of a loose strand of my hair. It made me laugh, and I stroked his cushion-like cheek.

We stepped through the green door into a small courtyard. An old woman was sitting on the stone floor in the shade, a piece of washed-out black fabric wrapped around her body and her head. Her legs, stretched out in front of her, were clad in dusty dark leggings. Black socks were in folds around her ankles. She was singing to herself, crushing Argan nuts with a stone. She did not look up.

"*Huile d'Argan*," Nashiema explained.

The courtyard was cool and smelled of sun-baked wood and stone. The walls were whitewashed and decorated with child-like drawings of fish in bright green and blue colours. Three doorways led off the yard into rooms. A flight of uneven stairs ran up onto the flat roof. Everything looked handmade, higgledy-piggledy and cosy.

I followed Nashiema into the kitchen. There was an almost complete lack of furniture, except for a badly built concrete shelf, which was holding a few glasses, some mismatched plates and an array of vegetables in various dried-out stages. A gas cylinder on the floor served for boiling water and cooking. There was no sink, no water tap.

A trapdoor in the kitchen floor gave access to a water cistern. A bucket tied to a rope was resting beside the door, waiting for the next plunge into the deep dark hole. The fresh water was precious and expensive, and was only used for drinking and cooking.

"What about washing?" I asked Nashiema, rubbing first my hands together, then the hems of my shirt.

"*Oho!*" Nashiema shook her head. She patted her hands and her dress - for washing - she made walking movements with her fingers and funny braying noises - we take the donkey. Then she drew a big circle with both arms and pointed vaguely towards the hilly backdrop - and go to the well.

"*Jour*," she added in French. With her flat hand she drew a line in front of her middle as if to cut the day in half.

Nashiema pointed at a small opening in the kitchen wall.

"*Shuf!*" she said.

I looked. Outside the kitchen, in a small courtyard, stood an undernourished donkey gorging on meagre kitchen waste. He was hung with empty plastic bottles and canisters as if to weigh him down and stop him from blowing away in the wind.

We left the kitchen. The next door led into a room, which was bare but for a place to sleep made from a heap of blankets on the stone floor.

I followed Nashiema to the staircase in the corner of the small yard. We climbed the worn concrete stairs and stepped onto the flat roof, which was merely the ceiling of the rooms below. Mattresses and cushions were strewn everywhere. Nashiema sat down with Samir. She took my hand and pulled me onto a cushion.

"*Shuf!*" She stretched out her arm and her finger followed the line of the horizon.

The ocean was lying beneath our feet, stretching into the distance, where it melted into the sky: a vast expanse of shades of blue and green.

I looked down onto a cluster of dwellings. The old stone-built part in the middle seemed to be the original building to which a growing family over generations had attached several habitations similar to Cherifa's house. Nashiema followed my eyes. She pointed at the stone building.

"Yassin," she said. "*Frère*."

There was no sign of Nashiema's brother or his family in their yard.

"*Atei!*" Cherifa's shrill voice travelled up to the terrace.

We jumped up from the cushions and climbed back down the steps into the courtyard. Nashiema stopped at one of the doorways. Before entering the living room, we shed our sandals, as is the custom in Morocco.

The room was rectangular, with a small opening near the ceiling to provide ventilation rather than a view.

A dark green raffia carpet covered part of the floor. Large cushions surrounded a low wooden table. A young woman of Nashiema's age was comfortably poised. She ogled me expectantly.

"Nadah!" Nashiema pointed at her. A long explanation in Berber followed, from which I gathered that Nadah was Nashiema's twin sister. Then she spent a long time speaking to Nadah, obviously explaining that my name was *Madame*, because Nadah shrieked cheerfully: "*La bes, Madame!*" She patted the cushion beside her.

"*La bes*, Nadah." Obediently I lowered myself down. Nadah and Nashiema were as different as day and night. Nadah was big-boned and strong, whereas Nashiema was petite and slender. Nadah was plain with crude features and crooked teeth, while Nashiema was exquisite and beautiful. Nadah seemed straightforward and uninhibited, while Nashiema was coy and reserved.

Nashiema left with Samir to help Cherifa with the tea. Nadah engulfed me in a cloud of henna-scented sympathy and

23

entertained me with unintelligible anecdotes from Taliouine, as it seemed. I did not understand much, but hearing her hearty laugh made me happy, made it seem as if we were old friends, sharing a joke, a bit of gossip. When all subjects were exhausted, Nadah jumped up and walked swiftly to the doorway, slipped into my sandals and paraded around the yard.

"*Madame, shuf*!" she called happily.

I nodded and watched in dismay my filigree sandals stretching from size four to seven. I expected the straps which had become pathetically thin strings to snap any minute. I sighed and made a note to buy sandals of a more robust nature the next time I visited the souk in Agadir. And maybe I should choose a bigger size just in case swapping shoes with Nadah became a habit.

In vain, I kept swatting a persistent group of flies away while looking around in the sparse room. A wooden cupboard, elaborately carved, held the family's possessions: a video, a bunch of plastic flowers in a bottle, blankets, photos, a small cuddly teddy, a copy of the *Koran*. The top of the cupboard was lined with tins of powdered baby milk. King Mohamed V was looking down on me from a poster on the wall.

There was nothing else in this room. My mind wandered through the rest of the house: the bare kitchen, the modest bedroom, the wonderful view from the roof – I realised that there was no toilet, no bathroom. I wondered if there were toilets in any of the other village houses. And if not, where did everybody go? How could they find privacy in a country where people were strolling around everywhere and at any time, stepping out of shadows and from behind bushes even in the most remote areas?

Nadah returned from her excursion and slumped back onto the cushion next to mine. She patted my hand and laughed.

"*Mezyan, Madame.*" She put her thumb up.

"I am glad you like them." I grinned.

I watched my abandoned shoes in the doorway shrink back to almost their former selves.

Cherifa appeared, balancing a tray with four narrow glasses, a steaming battered metal teapot, a few formless lumps of sugar and a bunch of fresh mint. She set the tray down on the wooden table.

Nashiema followed with a basket full of bread, a butter dish and a bowl with honey. Both women sat down on cushions. While Cherifa was preparing the tea, the three women chattered relentlessly in a language, which bore no similarity to any language I had heard before. Shrieks and giggles accompanied the conversation. Were they talking about the weather, the village, the donkey? Were they talking about me?

"I put her funny shoes on."

"Give her some of the old bread, Nashiema."

"And the rancid butter."

"Her sandals are smelly."

"What does she think she is doing coming up here and building a house?"

"And no husband!"

"Well, not surprising."

I felt a blush of embarrassment colouring my face. I wanted to leave but like being trapped in a nightmare, I was unable to move.

Cherifa stuffed the mint into the pot, followed by the lumps of sugar, which equalled at least ten teaspoons. After a while, she poured the tea out into the glasses, pulling the pot higher and higher so that the tea sloshed down like a splashing waterfall.

Nashiema held out the basket to me. She urged me to take some bread, which I knew was baked by the village women over Argan wood fire. Cherifa pushed the butter dish and the bowl of honey in front of me.

"*Mange, mange!*" she said pointing the food. She handed me a glass of mint tea.

I dipped and sipped, finding the butter and the bread fresh and tasty. Feeling the occasional friendly pat from Nadah, I started to relax. Even Cherifa's eyes did not seem so fearsome anymore. I listened to the women's chatter, the braying of a donkey nearby and the bleating of goats. Somewhere in the village, a female voice was singing strange high-pitched melodies from the mountains. I felt deeply contented, at peace. I

25

only ever experience this feeling in Morocco. It springs from the simplicity of life and the hospitality of the people. I have always had a strong yearning for Morocco during my periods of absence, a strange kind of bond, a love-hate affair, but I had never felt it as strongly as that day in Cherifa's house.

"*Ca va, Madame*?" Nadah beamed at me.

At that moment, I was sure that Cherifa and I would at least be able to get along if not become friends. I saw her invitation to tea as a positive sign. Nadah and Nashiema were so genuinely welcoming that I wondered why I ever harboured doubts as to whether I should buy the land or not.

Chapter Four

It was another glorious warm spring morning. I walked through the wide open doors of Agadir's only launderette just in time to see a gorgeous looking man with a mop of blond hair pull his T-shirt over his head and throw it into one of the battered looking washing machines.

The good thing about being a traveller is that you are more likely to stumble into unlikely situations I reflected gratefully whilst scrutinizing him discretely. He seemed straight out of the legendary television advert.

"Don't forget to wash your jeans!"

I gasped. Had I really said it? No, of course not, I wouldn't dare. I was a well-brought up woman, sophisticated and mature.

"Hi," I said casually, plucking my eyes off his well-shaped naked back. I dropped my bag with dirty washing in front of the nearest machine.

He spun round, blushing, and blinked apologetically. The colour of his eyes reminded me of mint. How suitable to come to Morocco.

"Oh – hi. Sorry," he murmured. "*Je suis desole.*"

"Not to worry," I said lightly, listening in surprise to the furious hammering of my heart. Thrown by the colour of his eyes I added: "Don't forget to wash your jeans."

Oh my God. I did say it. Clearly audible, it floated through the soap-scented air. With a mind of its own, it had slipped out of my mouth. Just when I was thinking how gorgeous this man was and that it would be quite nice to see a bit more of him. Blushing furiously I busied myself with my dirty washing, trying to hide my knickers between the towels on their way into the machine. He might not speak enough English to understand, I hoped. And maybe he did not watch television.

"My name is not Nick Kamen," he said with an adorable accent and laughed.

I was tempted to join my washing in the machine and thus disappear from this awkward situation.

"I don't mind. I mean - it doesn't matter. Forget it. I was being silly. I'm sorry."

Hastily, I slotted the coin into the machine, pressed the start button and almost ran out of the launderette, before he could think of anything to say. I was so embarrassed. I prayed I had not dropped a dirty sock, or worse, a pair of knickers onto the floor.

I walked as far away from the launderette as possible, wondering what had possessed me. I was too old for that. I didn't flirt. I hadn't flirted for years. I hardly even had personal conversations with men nowadays. The last time I fancied a man, I married him, which turned out to be a disastrous mistake. And here I was, struck by lust at first sight, uttering the world's most pathetic pickup line. He must have thought I was on my one-week holiday eager to find a fellow to keep me company.

I caught my reflection in the mirrored window of a café. Usually, I would hardly notice, but this time I stopped. I was embarrassed at the sight of myself. I was not used to it. It was like unexpectedly meeting my twin on the road of whom I had no idea she existed. I critically surveyed my reflection. My former mouse-coloured hair had succumbed to years of sunshine and shimmered in a lighter, more interesting shade. My skin was permanently suntanned, not to a leathery dark brown, but to a healthy sort of tone. I am not a tall person, but am compensated for the shortness by the fact, that my body is slim and easy maintenance. A few jogs, a bit of swimming, and I look and feel ok. I moved closer to the mirror.

There were new lines around my eyes. I panicked and pulled back. I was getting old. I was already more forty than thirty, and yet inside, I was still the same person as I was twenty years ago, more experienced, maybe, and slightly more mature. All those years have passed without me noticing. To me, a middle-aged woman has always been someone wearing shapeless brown skirts and sensible shoes, with a tired face devoid of any make-up and a hairdo to match – just a step away from a blue rinse. Now I was approaching middle age.

'Another reason to change my life,' I thought and returned to the encounter in the laundrette.

My washing would be finished before his and so I might not have to meet him again. I rushed back to the launderette and lurked around in the shadow outside, keeping a close eye on my watch. In time, I dashed inside, ready to pull out my washing as soon as the lights went off.

The good news was that no lone sock was lolling about on the floor.

The bad news was that he was there... He smiled when I entered. He hadn't washed his jeans, worse even; he had put a t-shirt on.

I nodded curtly and turned my attention to the washing to emphasise the fact that I was not searching for a lover and that I was using the laundrette solely for laundering. Angrily I realised that my clothes were not clean at all. In my hurry to get away, I had forgotten to add powder.

When I surfaced again, he was standing next to me. All blond and green-eyed and healthy-skinned and tanned, attractive in a friendly, reliable, decent way, with a lovely warm smile.

"Don't be – what do you say – embarrassed." He emphasised the last syllable. "It was fun."

"I am glad you enjoyed yourself," I said politely, thinking how sexy his accent was.

"My name is…" he began.

"I know... your name is Not Nick Kamen. You told me already. Have a good holiday, Not Nick." I laughed, slung my bag over my shoulder and left.

I stepped out into the bright sunshine and took the few steps down to the street. Agadir's only laundrette lived in one of the big hotels in the holiday quarter of the town. The quarter was purpose-built, crowded with noisy tourists and so far removed from the real Morocco and its people that it was one of my least favourite parts of Agadir, except for the beach. And the laundrette, of course.

I crossed the street, left the French, Chinese and Italian restaurants, English pubs and *Deutsche Kaffeestuben* behind and stepped onto the soft golden sand, which stretched towards the horizon, until, in the distance, it merged into a shallow sea. The tide was far out. I fought my way through rows and rows of sun chairs, on which mainly female tourists were sweating in the sun whilst being chatted up by young Moroccans, who were hoping to escape poverty through an invitation to Europe or better even, through marriage.

I fled towards the horizon until I was alone. I took off my sandals and bore my feet into the wet soft sand. Small waves came running, curiously chased around my buried feet and ran off again, carrying away the feeling of loneliness that had become my travel companion.

"That's all I need," I thought happily, "and this is the only country I want to be in."

Lunchtime was approaching and I turned to go back. The seafront looked beautiful. Hotels rose up like fantasies out of *Arabian Nights*, Moorish and whitewashed, with green roofs; a colour, which in the Islamic belief keeps the evil away. Palm trees swayed in the ocean breeze and the beach was golden. Even the snow-capped peaks of the Atlas Mountains were visible from some parts of the beach. It made a perfect shot for a holiday brochure

Life beyond the resort was different, though. Moroccan people struggled to find work or food for a family of seven or nine or more, or even a roof for the night. Most people were poor. Many were desperate. A few were very rich, residing in splendid villas near the King's palace, a couple of kilometres south of the holiday quarter. But there was also friendliness and hospitality, colours and scents, music and magic. Most of the package tourists would never see it, too frightened to venture out into the unknown and strange, too uncomfortable having to face the poverty or, worse, simply not interested.

I have not always loved Morocco as passionately as I do now. My first visit was a nightmare. From the moment I arrived in Tangier, I felt uncomfortable. I was hassled by children for presents, by men for cigarettes and sex, and by policemen for baksheesh. The different culture scared me, who had never set foot outside Europe before. The country was dry and dusty, and all I could smell was burning rubber and rotting rubbish. I had never witnessed poverty to such an extent before. My stomach turned into a firework after my first visit to a restaurant, a bug, from which I only completely recovered three months later. The moment I was back on European soil I could have wept with relief.

Over the following year, those memories gave way to others: the hospitality of people, prepared to share whatever little they had, white almond blossom covering the hills around Tafraoute like snow, the perfect peacefulness of a desert night, the simple life and food. Faces of Moroccans I had met popped up in my head, and I realised that I missed them. Memories like that wrapped themselves like blankets around the chilliness inside me. I returned the following winter and fell in love with the country and its people.

I had crossed the beach by now and reached the street, where I had left my vehicle. Fondly, I patted the battered side of my well-worn camper van which had been my house, my refuge, my friend and travel companion for the past seven years. I had dragged it up and down Europe during the summers and all through Morocco during the winters. We usually came to rest on the beaches around Taghazout where wild camping was still allowed. Whole colonies of European campers gathered on the beach, driven mostly by pensioners. Who else would have the time to spend the winter in Morocco? The odd lottery winner, perhaps, who arrived in a camper van the size of a coach with a Porsche under the built-in bed and a spa in the extendable bathroom. Or the gap-year-students, the unemployed and the so-called New Age Travellers, who came down here on a shoestring in ancient delivery vans with a mattress and a blanket in the rusty boot. And occasionally people like me, who had sold up and set off, to escape memories and to find a new, more satisfying life-style. Who found that they could not stop travelling and that it was exactly what they had been looking for.

However, for a while there had been a nagging feeling inside me. I had started to look longingly into lit up rooms in the evenings when driving through villages in the middle of nowhere, wondering what it would be like to live just there, to have friends, a washing machine, duties and a postman coming in the morning. I was not ready to live anywhere permanently, but needed to have a base. I wanted to throw an anchor because the freedom of life on the road was turning into a whirlwind threatening to carry me off mentally to a place of weightlessness, where I did not want to be.

It was then that Yassin told me about a little piece of land for sale in the hills behind Taghazout. Within days, my life had turned upside down. It was the moment on the beach in Agadir, with my feet buried in the wet sand and my body warmed by the sun that I knew I was going to do it. I was going to buy the piece of land and build a house on it.

I went to the bank and withdrew a rather large amount of money.

Chapter Five

I had been warned that the process of buying a piece of land in Morocco demands unlimited patience and tolerance and has a certain likeness to asking a four year old to tidy up his room. There is blame and bribe, goodwill but distraction, enthusiasm but delay. There are excuses and long stretches where nothing is being done at all. Those who have a tendency to frustration or anger are advised to refrain from purchasing anything more elaborate than round bread in Morocco.

With this in my mind, the words anger and frustration struck off my vocabulary and a winning smile on my lips, I strode along the dusty streets of Aourir to the notary's office. Salim followed behind, his threadbare *djellaba* blowing in the warm desert wind, shabby sandals flip-flopping madly as he tried to catch up with me. He coughed and splattered, nearly losing his precious cigarette out of the corner of his mouth.

The notary's office was in a white washed breezeblock building. Uneven cement steps led upstairs into a cool room, furnished with three senile looking wooden chairs on one side and a fragile desk, bending under the weight of a computer, on the other. Behind the monitor, a slumbering secretary woke with a start.

"*Monsieur le Notaire*?" I asked the man when he had woken sufficiently.

He answered in Berber, and from Salim's swift gravitation towards the chairs I could tell he had asked us to sit down and wait.

Here we were, sitting, waiting for the notary: Salim, the secretary and I with no language in common, in almost deadly silence had it not been for the buzzing of flies and the murmur of street-life floating in through the cracks in the window frame.

The air was stale and smelled of paper and sweat mixed with the scent of stewing *tajines*, which occasionally wafted in from the street.

The floor was covered with faded black and white tiles. They were diamond-shaped and ran in lines across the floor like sharp zigzags. Light – dark – light – dark. When I bent my head, the effect was completely different. On shutting one eye and concentrating hard, the floor became three-dimensional.

After half an hour, the smile had gone from my lips and my patience was being challenged.

"Hitler good man," the secretary suddenly shouted out, jumped up and gave me an appreciative thumbs-up.

I stared at him, wondering why I was always so easily identified as being of German origin and worse, wrongly believed to be an admirer of the former dictator.

"No, he was not," I retorted.

The man sank back onto his chair, shook his head and muttered unintelligible words into the collar of his *djellaba*.

There was nothing to do. I was drawn back to the mystery of the floor tiles. There were a hundred and twenty tiles from the door to the window, seventy tiles from the chairs to the desk. Every line ended with half a diamond, but for some reason the lines further towards the desk ended with a whole diamond, followed by a little blue square squeezed in. I was unable to work out why and it irritated me.

I gave up and leant back. A group of flies were chasing around in large ovals, from window to door and back to the window in fruitless attempts to escape the stuffy room. I felt pity for them. And for me.

Salim belched loudly. I moved a chair further trying to escape the fumes emanating from his mouth.

I was bored. Salim was bored. To busy himself he started picking his nose. Nose picking is not seen as rude behaviour in Morocco, but a normal and necessary part of the daily hygiene, similar to cleaning hands or brushing hair. I shuddered.

My eyes wandered to the more pleasant sight of young King Mohamed V, who smiled down at me from a poster on the otherwise bare wall. I smiled back, thinking about the land I was about to buy.

The telephone rang, startling the secretary. I stood up. After a machine gun like exchange into the receiver, he announced breezily:

"*Monsieur le notaire a du retard.*"

I sank back onto the chair.

The secretary gave me a suspicious glance and shook his head.

"Hitler ... he no good man?" he asked, searching my face.

"Is a murderer a good man?" I asked back.

The secretary deflated once more to an unhappy heap behind his desk.

Salim had fallen asleep, his head leaning against the wall, which was decorated with a grey greasy line, where generations of people have rested their heads waiting for a delayed notary. His half-opened mouth was puffing and blobbing like an ancient hot water boiler. I closed my eyes.

"*Bonjour, Madame, Messieurs.*"

The secretary jumped up once again. Monsieur Abderrahim, the notary, had arrived.

Salim grunted and sat up. Monsieur Abderrahim placed a stack of papers on the secretary's desk, then turned round and bowed slightly in my direction. He broke into a smile, which not only lit up his face but also the whole room, stressing the evenness of his features, the intensity of his dark eyes. He strode across the room, unlocked the door to his office.

"*Entrez, s'il vous plait.*"

Monsieur Abderrahim's office was as sparsely furnished as the reception room and dominated by a metal desk covered with piles of paper. The only modern gadget was a complicated looking mobile phone, which was sucking energy out of a socket near the door.

"*Assez-vous.*" The notary pointed at two plastic chairs in front of the desk. "*Comment puis-je vous aider?* "

As he spoke French, I struggled to explain our matter of concern in the same language. He listened carefully, then took Salim's papers of ownership and studied them for a while.

I moved around on my chair. One of the reasons why it was so difficult to buy land in this country was the fact that the plots were on average owned by seven brothers and sisters, out of whom one did not want to sell at all, one was not contactable, one had died and left his part to his six children and the remaining four were arguing over the price.

"There should not be any problems. Salim is the sole owner of the land," he finally said. "Have you agreed a price?"

I remembered the day when I met Salim in Yassin's café to finalise our deal. Salim crouched on a chair watching me anxiously as I climbed up the steps to the terrace. I knew he depended so much on the sale, because he owed money to many people, who were demanding immediate repayment. His gaunt body was resting tiredly against the table, sunken into his torn and dirty *djellaba*.

"Salim, *la bes*," I said and sat down.

He grinned and started rolling a cigarette, which looked like the anorexic sister of a matchstick. His hands were shaking. There were rumours about Salim drinking.

"*Bonjour,* Kate," Yassin appeared on the terrace, wiping his hands in a dirty dishcloth. "Had a good night?"

"Thank you, yes," I said. "We need to agree a price."

Life shot into Salim's tormented body and anguished soul. His cigarette dropped out of his shaking hands but he did not pay any attention. He sat up straight and named a ludicrously high price.

It was unacceptable. I named the sum, which I was prepared to pay. Salim shook his head and mumbled something unfriendly sounding. His body deflated again. Yassin pleaded with him until he finally reduced his price considerably. But it was still nowhere near my offer. I refused. Salim grew angry, shouting words I was glad I not to be able to understand. I got up to leave. Yassin clung on to the promise of a commission and tried desperately to mediate.

We haggled for a long time until we met somewhere in the middle. From Salim's point of view, it must have still been a satisfying outcome because his mouth remained twisted into a rare smile however much he tried to hide it.

"Yes, we have agreed a price," I answered.

"Then we can proceed with the purchase," Monsieur Abderrahim continued. "May I have the money, please?"

I was glad to get rid of it. As the Moroccan currency did not seem to include notes above fifty dirham, every withdrawal came as a substantial wad with a brown paper bag to match. I watched the bag disappear in the top drawer of the notary's desk instead of a proper safe. I was not given a receipt. Salim pulled several keys out of his pockets, which joined my money in the drawer.

"Please give me your passports now," Monsieur Abderrahim said, after he had locked the drawer.

Salim and I handed over our identities, and the notary started writing out the *contrat de vente*. By hand. In Arabic. I watched for a while how ornate letters were pouring out of the notary's pencil. It was like observing an artist creating a masterpiece. Fascinating though it was, it took a long time. I started to shift on the hard chair.

Finally, Monsieur Abderrahim put his pen down and stood up.

"Please wait outside until the contract is ready for you to sign," he requested politely.

We left the office. Monsieur Abderrahim handed the contract over to the secretary. Once again, Salim and I found ourselves on the fragile chairs in the reception room. While the secretary was struggling with the keyboard, Salim dozed off and I returned to trying to solve the mystery of the floor pattern.

It took almost an hour until we were called back into the office.

By then, I was nearly beside myself with boredom and the palpable sense of the walls closing in around me.

"I will translate this contract into French for you. Please tell me if everything is all right," Mr Abderrahim said after he had asked us to sit down.

I hoped very much it was. I had spent enough time in this office.

Unfortunately, my nationality had been put down wrongly. Swiftly, Mr Abderrahim headed back to the secretary.

The office seemed too small for Salim and me together. I could hardly breathe. There were noises and smells and movements which made me shudder. We waited for half an hour, silently and uneasily, wondering if they had all gone for lunch. Salim started to pick his nose again.

"Yuk," I said quietly.

Monsieur Abderrahim returned. He translated the whole contract again, and on finding all personal details entered correctly, he said, "Please sign now."

I signed, thinking that never before in my life I had signed a contract typed in beautiful Arabic letters.

I must admit that I did not understand every word. My French was not good enough to grasp the contents without seeing the words written on paper and I had to more or less sign on trust. I did trust Monsieur Abderrahim. What reason would he have to cheat on me?

Salim signed with a limp looking "S". It resembled the crude drawing of a sickly snake and seemed to exhaust his literary skills.

"Would you like the contract translated into French?" Mr Abderrahim said. "It will take about ten days, *insha'allah*."

Insha'allah! So God will! It was often added in Morocco when talking about a time scale to transfer responsibility in the most possible case of delay. It would take a while to get hold of the translation, but I nodded and agreed to pay a small fee for the service, so that one day in the distant future, I would be able to find out what I had signed.

"What happens next, Monsieur Abderrahim?" I asked.

"Your signatures have to be certified by an official."

"Where can we do that?"

Mr Abdullah suggested the town hall of Agadir. I looked at my watch. Half past eleven. In half an hour, the whole of Morocco would retreat to a four-hour lunch break and bring life to a standstill - a true legacy of the French.

At five minutes to twelve, I chased Salim up the steps of the ugly concrete building that was Agadir's town hall. In no time, we had made it to the right official, a grim looking clerk behind a glass window. He glanced shortly at Salim's passport, threw it back at him with a flood of harsh words and slammed the shutters of his little booth. Lunchtime!

I grabbed Salim's passport. It had expired five years ago! My heart sank. Still, there was no need to humiliate him like that. Poor Salim! Desperate for the sale to go through, he begged for mercy, but the shutters remained shut.

We raced back to Aourir and found Mr Abderrahim still in his office.

"What shall I do now?" I asked him after I had spilled out the unfortunate story.

Mr Abderrahim smiled calmly. "Take Salim to the town hall in Taghazout. He is known there and you will not have any difficulties."

Why had he sent me to the distant Agadir in the first place, when everything could have been done practically at home? He must have realised that Salim's passport had expired, when he set up the contract. I was confused. I remembered the contract I

39

had signed. On trust. I earnestly hoped I had not sold my possessions. Or made a generous monetary donation towards the notary's living expenses. Or, worst of all, married Salim.

Salim and I drove back to Taghazout. The car was overheated. By now, I was tired of being with him in the office, in the car, in the street. The town hall in Taghazout was shut and would only open at half past two. I fled to Yassin's café for a little bit of Salim-free time and a chat. I sank onto one of the chairs on his shady terrace. There were no other guests. Most people had eaten by now. Yassin appeared with a plate full of fried fish, bread and two glasses of mint tea and sat down to share it with me.

"Eat, Kate, and then tell me about your morning," he said, tearing a piece off the round loaf and thrusting it into my hand.

Carefully, I spooned up some of the fish with it. It was delicious. Freshly caught and fried with garlic, lemon and coriander: exactly how I liked it.

"Yassin, you are so good to me." I sighed while mopping up the herb infused oil with my bread.

Yassin closely inspected the holes in his dishcloth, pretending not to hear.

After I had finished, I told him about the morning. He laughed about poor Salim imploring the closed shutters to open again.

"It is not very nice of you, Yassin," I said, trying to keep a straight face.

In no time, it was half past two and Salim and I were back together, waiting in the cool, marbled reception of the town hall to be dealt with.

After half an hour, we were called to the desk, which was so high, that I almost had to stand on my tiptoes to be able to see the clerk. He was hardly taller, and our eyes met just above the cool polished surface. I explained our problem. As predicted, Salim was well known in Taghazout and there was no need for a valid passport. I handed the contract over to the clerk.

We waited for a long time. Numerous handwritten entries had to be made into a large book. Every entry demanded at least three different stamps. Every signature, every date, every dot had to be certified with another array of stamps. As soon as the clerk moved his hand, it had to be stamped, dated and certified in true French style.

I had to cross the busy main road several times to acquire two-dirham-stamps at the kiosk, which I had to hand over to the clerk as a way of payment for the different papers I was about to receive. Meticulously, the clerk glued one of the stamps onto each page and, with short brisk movements, placed a selection of rubber stamps around. Then he looked at it from a slight distance like an artist critically surveying his work, with his head angled this way and that way and his brows furrowed. After a while, he added his signature with flourish, placed within the group of paper and ink stamps in an arrangement pleasing to the eye, at least to his. I was too ignorant to understand why he would spend so much time on this job.

Hours later, I left the town hall in irritation. Yet, I was the proud owner of three sets of papers, beautifully stamped, stapled and signed.

For Salim, who could neither read nor write and who did not know anything about the wonders of French bureaucracy, the afternoon was wasted. He had shifted and sighed, he had tapped and moaned and only the thought of money had kept him in the town hall. I had entertained myself with nightmarish daydreams about what it would be like if I woke up one morning and found Salim had become my Siamese twin.

Once again, Salim and I drove to Aourir; once again back to the notary's office. The deal was done quickly and unceremoniously. Mr Abderrahim unlocked his drawer. He handed the keys over to me and gave the wad of money to Salim. With a sigh of relief, Salim stuffed the money under his *djellaba*, which made him look as if he was pregnant.

I paid another huge lump of money to Mr Abderrahim for the registration of the land in my name.

"You can pick up the contract and registration in ten days, *insha'allah*," Mr Abderrahim told me.

Ten days insha'allah seemed to be the timescale for paperwork of all sorts.

I gave Salim a lift back to Taghazout and dropped him outside the village at his request. Maybe he was going to dig a hole for the money he was carrying. It was probably the safest hiding place.

"Be careful," I warned him. I watched him disappear up the hill, a bent figure in a billowing *djellaba*.

From his passport, I knew he was forty-eight, but he looked like sixty-eight. He was carrying a fortune. People would murder for less. He lived in a Moroccan equivalent of a bed-sit in a very run down part of the village. He was a rich man now. I wondered what he was going to do with the money – if there was any left after paying off his debts!

On my own, driving into Taghazout, I started feeling euphoric. I had bought a piece of land. I was going to build a house. This was going to be my new home. I was now one of 'them', part of this community. Hurray! My hands were drumming on the steering wheel.

I bought a bottle of Coke to celebrate with Yassin.

"You need a builder," Yassin stated perfectly reasonably, pulling me off my cloud.

"I know, Yassin. But where can I find one?"

Finding a builder seemed to me a gigantic milestone, probably the size of the Atlas Mountain range. Would I be able to find a local builder or would I have to go to Agadir? The local builders were likely to speak only Berber and Arabic. The builders from Agadir were known to be very expensive and maybe not even prepared to venture as far out as Taliouine.

It dawned on me that this was not going to be the only hurdle on my way to becoming a proud house owner. However, I was determined to take each one of them with ease.

DOWN TOWARDS THE SEA

Chapter Six

I woke up early the next morning. The need to find a builder and to get started on my project drove me out of my camper van. The morning sun was spreading like a cosy blanket over the night-chilled beach. It was going to be another clear and warm spring day. Despite the number of camper vans stationed here it was still quiet. Hardly anybody was up yet. Only the occasional jogger or dog walker had left a trail on the immaculate post-tidal beach.

The sea was far out and the thunder of waves muffled by the distance. Sandals in my hand, I padded over acres of wet sand towards Taghazout. Swarms of hungry seagulls circled above a group of fishermen, who were gutting their catch. A gang of wild dogs loitered near, ready to fall onto the discarded guts, but wary of the birds, which defended their breakfast with sharp beaks.

I reached the fishing village, rounded the corner by climbing over rocks and soon walked along the crescent shaped beach of Taghazout. The former simple fishermen's dwellings had been extended and renovated, painted pink or white and fitted with bright blue shutters. Each building was charmingly imperfect with rounded edges and handmade uneven plaster. Thick black electricity cables crisscrossed the scene like a young child's angry scribble. There were acres of roof terraces. Some were covered with bamboo or palm leaves to provide shelter from the sun. Others were overgrown with pink and purple bougainvillea. Palm trees stretched their filigree leaves towards the sun.

The middle of the beach was lined with wooden rowing boats, which the fishermen used night after night; shiny black boats, each with a brightly coloured rim.

A group of fishermen were coming in with their nightly catch. I stopped to watch their arrival. The heavy boats had to be carried up the beach, out of reach of the high tide or in case of a sudden storm. Three strong wooden poles were pushed through the oarlocks on the rim on each side of the boat. Six men got hold of the ends, lifted the boat with an enormous effort and carried it quickly up the beach, their faces distorted by the strain and their legs in danger of giving way under the weight.

I walked past a rectangular low building, a functional design and remarkably out of place in the jumbled array of beachfront houses. Here, the freshly caught fish was auctioned every morning at ten o'clock. Fishermen were already streaming inside through the wide open door, hoping for a good price for their catch. The speed of the auction fascinated me: the string of Berber numbers, repetitive and soothing like a shipping forecast on the radio, which only stopped when the auction was over.

I mingled with the men and was swept through the door into a cool clinical room, covered from top to bottom in sparkling white tiles. It was immaculately clean. In the middle of the hall, there was stage onto which the fishermen dumped their buckets, baskets, crates and casks full of fish, shells, prawns, crabs and octopus.

Most of the poor creatures seemed to have accepted their fate and were lying still except for the occasional flapping of a tail or a fin. The crabs rushed around in the baskets trying to escape, but were firmly locked in. The octopuses were fighting hard to get away, moving and sliding constantly: a slimy mass of flesh and tentacles, slithering effortlessly and silently over edges of boxes and buckets, fast and furious, determined to make it back to the sea. But they never got far. Rough hands plucked the creatures off the floor and threw them back into the containers, from where they tirelessly started another escape.

A young man arrived, dressed in a suit, with an unsmiling face: the auctioneer. The chatter stopped. Anticipation filled the room. The auctioneer jumped onto the stage, and a monotonous chanting in Berber and Arabic descended on us.

Yassin appeared by my side, buying fish for his restaurant.

"You want octopus? I will make for you," he offered and pulled one up, which had wound itself around his shoe. I looked at the struggling creature.

"No thank you, Yassin, not today," I answered.

"What do you do today?" he enquired.

"I need to find a builder."

Yassin grinned. "Very good. I have very good builder for you from Taghazout. You speak to him. You come to café at eight tomorrow."

What would I do without my friend Yassin? I hoped that we would never fall out, at least not as long as building was in progress.

I arrived at Yassin's café at eight the next morning.

"*Bonjour*, Yassin." I slumped onto a chair.

The terrace was filled with the earthy scent of freshly brewed coffee.

"It will be hot today," Yassin grumbled, vigorously wiping the plastic tablecloth with a sponge.

The flowery patterns had long faded due to his generous use of bleach. My throat started to feel scratchy.

"You should wear gloves, Yassin, or you'll end up with hands looking three times your age."

He stood up and looked at me for the first time this morning, a baseball cap as usual covering the balding spot on the top of his head.

"And you will be banned from this café if you always know everything better," he said.

45

Yassin was definitely not a morning person, yet he waved across the road, where his brother Mohamed was opening the wooden shutters to his shop. It was a garage-sized stall with a counter in the front, from behind which he served his customers with nearly everything from pegs to potatoes.

Yassin wiped his forehead with the back of his lower arm, dripping bleach from the dirty sponge down his Manchester United t-shirt.

"We have breakfast?"

"Great idea." I jumped up from my chair. "What shall I do?"

"Sit down and wait." He collected his cleaning utensils and went inside. The slapping noise of his flip-flops echoed across the tiled floor.

I looked around. He had already been busy. Salt and pepper barrels were neatly arranged in the centre of each table next to ashtrays and glasses with serviettes. Yassin made the serviettes himself by tearing small rectangles out of sheets of paper.

Mohamed on the other side of the road had already been to the souk in Agadir. Whistling, he unloaded wooden crates of fresh vegetables and fruit from his small van and arranged them in front of his stall. Soon a colourful array of tomatoes, beans, potatoes, bananas and oranges lit up the street. Mohamed stacked bunches of mint and coriander on his counter and I could almost smell the strong herbal scent.

The first Berber music of the day reached my ears. Another stall had opened its shutters. Two boys were carrying a wooden stretcher piled high with rounds of bread from the bakery on the hill down into the village to distribute them to the stalls and cafés.

Yassin returned with two glasses of hot milky coffee, a basket of fresh bread and a glass bowl of honey with a piece of comb in the middle. He arranged everything on the table and sat down.

"Eat, Kate," Yassin said, tearing a piece off the loaf and dipping it into the bowl.

"When will the builder come?" I asked wiping a sticky drop of honey off my chin.

"Soon now, *insha'allah*," Yassin bumbled in his customary English. "You wait here."

He drained his coffee, cleared the table and went inside his café to prepare the *tajines* for lunch.

Insha'allah. That meant he might not come at all. I sighed and prepared myself to spend the day on Yassin's terrace.

After I had drunk several mint teas, counted the customers in Mohamed's stall and learnt the words of Khaleb's *Aicha* by heart I ran out of ideas how to entertain myself. I was fed up with having to wait, not being at all one with the *insha'allah* approach to life. I was just about to jump up and leave - the café, the village, the country - when the builder arrived. It was ten o'clock. His name was also Yassin. He could only speak Berber. My friend Yassin offered to translate.

Yassin-the-builder was the chubbiest Moroccan I had ever seen. Overweight people are an unusual sight in Morocco. Due to the lack of money, most of them were on a meagre diet, but the builder was obviously better off. He waddled into the café and sank onto a chair. His eyes, embedded in his plump face, glanced at me briefly, and I thought he would spit on the floor. He did not greet me. He spoke to my friend Yassin as if I were not there.

"What is he saying, Yassin?" I asked.

"He says: fifty thousand," Yassin murmured, examining the crusty remains of *tajine* on his t-shirt.

"Fifty thousand!" No wonder the builder looked so well nourished. "It is too much, Yassin."

The unintelligible exchange continued, dominated by gunfire of demands from the builder. I watched my friend trying to keep up with his pace.

"What now, Yassin?"

"He says: thirty thousand."

"Still too much, tell him."

Sma cha. smali bsef alcham. Wacha. Oho, lasam smala.

"Twenty thousand." My friend wiped small beads of sweat off his forehead.

"That sounds much better. What exactly will I get for it?"

Smacha wali bacha ifulki.

Yassin shrugged his shoulders. "Your house." He re-arranged the salt and pepper barrels.

Wacha.

The builder tried to clean his fingernails with a key.

I had no idea what he was talking about. There was no mention of plans or detailed cost. The builder's approach was simple: I build a house and you pay for it. He must have thought I was a sad pushover, who would part with a ludicrous amount of money and let him build whatever he fancied. I got up and left the café. And the village.

What a depressing beginning! Would I ever be able to find a builder?

Chapter Seven

The sun was hot. I was back inside my newly acquired four walls, imagining different layouts and designing the interior of my future home. A warm wind slipped in and out through decaying breezeblocks, in its wake a collection of sun-baked mountain village scents: a thyme-like smell mixed with dung and hot dust. I was sitting in the shade, leaning against the wall, a picnic of flat round bread, apricot jam and oranges spread out in front of me. My purple geranium was thriving in its sheltered solitude and I shared my water with her. I shut my eyes and listened to the lunchtime-quietness of the village. Nobody was around. A chicken clucked. A dog howled in the distance.

The sound of sandaled feet flapping along the path interrupted the peacefulness. I could not imagine anybody going for a walk in the midday heat. Voices were chatting animatedly. In English, as it turned out, when the group stopped outside my house. I jumped up and peered through a hole in the breezeblock wall only to find myself eye to eye with a group of red-faced middle-aged tourists with unsuitable clothing. The women sported short skirts and sleeveless tops. The men wore shorts and socks pulled up almost to their knees. The group stared at my walls.

"…bought by an English woman," a voice said with a strong Arabic accent and a hint of admiration.

I rushed to the next hole and stared out at a Moroccan man, who was presumably the herdsman. He had fashionably long and curly hair. I had never seen him before.

My fellow country people were enraptured.

"Marvellous view."

"Clever investment."

"Bit primitive, though."

"Imagine – no toilet, no water."

"…bloody brave of her."

I held my breath and dreaded the moment when they would knock on my door, but I was lucky.

The group walked on. I heard them being whisked into Cherifa's house, probably to have tea for wildly inflated prices.

Peacefulness was restored once more. I busied myself with separating the remnants of Salim's building work and tidying them into heaps of sand, breezeblocks and gravel, making whole armies of lizards temporarily homeless and dash confusedly around for safety.

A knock on my rusty metal door interrupted this satisfying task.

My first visitor! I pull the door open with vigour. It bounced back and propelled me towards a young man with his hands in his trouser pockets and a grin on his face. His hair and moustache were black, as were his eyes. He wore a white t-shirt sporting the logo of a well-known western manufacturer, a faded pair of jeans and hiking boots, which, judging by the soles' determination to separate from the rest of the shoes, seemed to be on their last legs. He looked like a male version of Nashiema. No doubt, it was her brother Yassin, whose habitat was somewhere in the middle of Cherifa's cluster of add-ons.

"Yassin?" I asked, rubbing my throbbing shoulder. It occurred to me that men were either called Yassin or Mohamed. If my circle of acquaintances grew, it would become difficult to distinguish between them.

My visitor broke into a lazy smile. His white teeth lit up his dark face and his eyes sparkled.

"Madame - *atei*," he said.

"*Shokran*." I was pleased. Another invitation to tea.

"*Azih*." Yassin waved his hand and turned back.

I stepped out of my house and locked the door. It was only a short distance to walk, past Cherifa's house and down a narrow side path. We entered Yassin's home through a small wooden gate set in a beautiful old stonewall and found ourselves in a tiny yard, from which a doorway led into the only room. The floor in the yard was covered with layers of stone and dried mud. A young woman was kneeling on the floor, trying to clean a toddler's face with a cloth.

"Mina - *femme*." Yassin pointed at his wife.

"Jalal." He looked at the little boy and proudly held two fingers in the air.

I wanted to pick him up, this tiny dark man with eyes like fresh chestnuts, and give him a great big hug, but he was hiding shyly behind his mother. His little shirt and shorts were torn and holey. Mina shook Jalal off, jumped up and laughed. She adjusted her colourful headscarf and straightened her long cotton dress over her pregnant belly.

"*La bes, Madame*." Her big smile made me feel good. She grabbed my hand and patted it. A round little face with a snub nose and big round eyes; she was probably not older than eighteen.

Giggling and bubbling, Mina ushered me with short Berber words and tongue clicking into the only room as if I was a chicken.

Hrish, hrish, hrish.

The sharp "r" sounded like tearing textile.

She urged me to sit down on the bed, which had been turned into a sofa with the help of a yellow blanket and big cushions with gold trimmings. A sweet heavy perfume emanated from the cushions. I looked around. The only other piece of furniture in this cell-like room was the customary ornately carved cupboard, which held Mina and Yassin's possessions.

51

They were displayed behind the glass doors: a few glasses, a turquoise cuddly bunny, two toy cars, a few colourful ornaments decorated with plastic flowers, a video cassette, but no television, a couple of CDs, but no CD player. The ceiling of the whitewashed, plastered room was lined with sticks. Strong branches were put across every thirty centimetres and in between, the spaces were filled with twigs. I liked the look of it and decided to do the same in my little Berber house.

Mina and Yassin sat down on the green and yellow raffia carpet, which covered the concrete floor. Yassin had brought out the gas cylinder and lit it to boil water for the tea. Mina shook some flour into a flat wooden bowl, added water and yeast and made dough for bread. She parted the dough and rolled it into small balls, whilst smiling and chatting to me. I did not understand a word, but it made me feel comfortable, and our unintelligible conversation flowed.

Djef bsa, smella bezef.

"I like your little house."

Smcha wacha amen hrish.

"It is kind of you to invite me."

Wacha.

Yassin went over to the cupboard to fetch glasses for the tea. He returned with three odd ones. He explained that they only had three glasses. The fourth glass broke last week.

I slid off the bed and joined Mina and Yassin on the floor. The chatter never ceased, and even though we did not understand each other well it avoided embarrassing silence. We talked and tried to explain but failed to understand most of the time, which made us laugh. Mina giggled and chirped like a little bird. Her smile stretched over her whole face, closing her eyes to slits. She and Yassin were teasing and laughing together in an affectionate way. Jalal stood at a safe distance near the doorway, pressing against the wall. He smiled cautiously at me; huge eyes were fixed on my face.

The water was boiling and Yassin stuffed mint and sugar into the kettle. Mina took over the gas cylinder. She rolled the dough balls out into flat rounds and baked them in a pan. A delicious scent of mint and fresh bread wafted through the small room. Jalal pushed himself along the wall nearer to his mother. When the bread was ready and cooling in a basket, Mina whisked some eggs together and poured them into the hot pan. Finally, the gas cylinder was put out into the yard. Mina placed the pan on the floor in our middle. Lunch was ready. Jalal settled closely beside his mother.

"*Mange, mange*!" Yassin invited me, handing me a large chunk of the warm bread.

We drank tea and scooped up the egg with fresh bread, the four of us eating from one pan. It was a refreshingly simple meal. The hospitality touched me. After we had eaten, I went to my house and fetched the two oranges I had left over. Yassin cut them into wedges and handed them round. I pushed mine on to Jalal who was sucking noisily with his eyes shut. The juice ran down his little face, leaving trails on his dust-covered skin.

I felt welcome. I liked Mina and Yassin. Apart from finding the right builder, things seemed to be going well.

In the evening, I joined my friend Yassin on the terrace of his café.

"Meet Yassin-the-builder again," Yassin suggested. "He wants to talk."

"Oh come on, Yassin, he doesn't want to talk to me. He doesn't even look at me. I don't want to meet him again."

"You are like a child. You want a good builder – he is a good builder." Yassin's fingers were drumming on the table.

"Last time he ignored me."

"He is Moroccan man. Very traditional. Is used to working with men. I know it is difficult, but he is a good builder," Yassin insisted.

After a while he continued. "I heard that Cherifa will build two rooms on top of her house, when Nadah marries Philippe, for them to live in."

I sat up. "Another floor? Are you joking?"

"I am not joking."

This could not be! Here I had found the perfect place with a view to die for and Cherifa was going to build a second floor, when Nadah married Philippe. When would this be and who was Philippe, anyway?

Yassin shrugged his shoulders.

Should it happen, I would be looking at the whitewashed walls of Cherifa's house instead of the sea and the sunset. I had to change my plans. What if I also had two floors? I should end up a few centimetres above Cherifa, because I was slightly higher up the hill. I did not want two floors. On the other hand, I wanted the unobstructed view. Why build here at all, if this was not going to happen?

I stared at the merry bustling on the terrace of Café Copacabana.

"You need candles, Yassin. I will bring you candles from Agadir."

"You come at ten tomorrow? Speak to the builder?"

"And maybe some napkins." I got up to leave. I had to re-design my house.

"Ten o'clock?"

"Yes, Yassin, yes."

For the rest of the evening, I weighed the pro and cons of either house. It was difficult. I loved the little Berber house I had envisaged, with a courtyard and one or two rooms around it, with whitewashed walls and sticks under the ceiling. But I also loved the sunset. It turned out that I loved the sunset just a tiny bit more than the little Berber house.

I drew and erased, added a floor, drew again and crossed out, scrunching up page after page and littering the floor of my van with white paper balls. I bit the end of my pencil until it split, filling my mouth with small splinters. Disgusted, I threw the pencil down amongst the paper balls. My plans were finished.

My little Berber house had transformed into a small villa. There was an open plan living and cooking area, a bathroom and a bedroom. Steps were going up to a second floor. Half of the second floor would become a landing and a bedroom, the other half a south-facing terrace. From the terrace, steps would lead up to the top of the bedroom, to my roof terrace, providing a three hundred and sixty degree view. I would be residing above the village like in a watchtower and see the sunset every night.

I spent the best part of the night building a little cardboard model of my planned house in order to overcome language problems and to get myself used to the rather uninspiring appearance of the villa. I also drew a reasonably professional looking plan.

I was not sure about the benefits of such a meeting, but arrived at the café in time the next morning. Maybe Yassin-the-builder had miraculously changed into a pleasant and co-operative man.

He had not changed into a man who arrived on time, for sure, because he was four-and-a-half hours late. By that time, I had walked the whole length of the beach and back, had had lunch and countless glasses of mint tea. I could have driven to Marrakesh, flown to England or sailed across to the Canary Islands in the same time, but every time I was about to call the meeting off, my friend Yassin pushed another mint tea in front of me.

"I guess that Yassin-the-builder has promised you an astronomical commission if the deal went ahead," I muttered.

Yassin sat down. Before he could answer the plump builder waddled into the café and forced his expansive body onto a chair at our table. He hardly acknowledged me, let alone apologise for his delay. He was unshaven and smelled of cement and fish. I spread my plans out on the table and placed the cardboard model on top. The builder did not look at it once. He burped, unrestrained, as it is custom in Morocco. I tried not to breathe in and to smile pleasantly at the same time. He talked to Yassin, picking invisible crumbs off the table and sounding altogether uninterested.

"Twenty three thousand," my friend Yassin translated.

"For what, Yassin?" I almost shouted with frustration. "I drew these plans, Yassin, the lay-out of my house. I built this little model, in case the plans are too difficult to read. And he does not even look at them. Does he not understand?"

Yassin shrugged his shoulders.

"I will explain the plans to you, Yassin, and you explain it to him."

My friend nodded unhappily, while the builder seemed to be about to get up.

"This is the kitchen area, you see, Yassin, and I need a wall here and here, for the bathroom and the bedroom downstairs and a staircase here in the corner..."

"In which corner? A staircase? Why you need staircase?" my friend Yassin asked.

I sighed. I should have stayed with the simple one-storey Berber dwelling: one courtyard, two rooms going off, flat roofs with mattresses strewn everywhere. I was making it too complicated. Yassin tried hard to understand and communicate my plans, and the builder nearly fell asleep with boredom.

I could imagine the discourse of their conversation:

"I really don't understand what she wants."

"Don't bother, I wouldn't do it anyway the way she wants. I don't like these Europeans with their pockets full of money. Especially not women!"

"But that money is going to go into your pocket!"

"Yeah, I quite like that. Okay, tell her: twenty three thousand."

"Twenty three thousand? For what?"

"Well, whatever!"

I realised that I was not getting anywhere. The builder got up and walked out.

Later, I was walking back to my van along the beach to clear my head. The day was ending. I loved the hour before the sun disappeared into the sea. The pace of nature slowed down before the great climax. People made their way home in anticipation of a meal. Seagulls landed on the beach in groups to settle down for the night.

I felt good on this beach, these kilometres of sand and sea, wild and natural. It was a miracle. I looked along the community of campers. Unfortunately, the number had increased about ten times within the last seven years. It was another reason to move up into the mountains. There was not enough room for so many different types of people to live peacefully together.

The sun hovered above the sea as if to test the temperature of the water before descending into it. A group of camels trotted along, black humpy shadows against the orange sky. I savoured the moments before the sunset. The waves were less noisy. The temperature was less soaring. The wild dogs curled up amongst the pack and lost their fierceness. There was a sense of relief everywhere. A cool mist rose, smelling of sea and salt.

I sat down on the sand and felt the humidity rising. My shirt became clammy. Soon it would be dark.

"*Madame*! You need builder? You speak to Yassin. My brother. Tomorrow, two o'clock. Hassan's supermarket."

I looked up into a familiar face, which I could not place.

"Fine," I answered tiredly. Another builder. Another Yassin. "The more the merrier."

Chapter Eight

Impatient knocking on the door of my van woke me up early the next morning, from a nightmare featuring an overweight builder, who was trying to set fire to a cardboard house. Still half immersed in the dream, I pulled the door open. Outside stood Abdullah, one of the young Moroccans, who sold bread to the campers.

There were many young bread sellers and the competition was fierce. From dawn, the boys would cruise around the camping cars on their rusty bicycles, baskets full of freshly baked bread strapped to the back. Like hawks, they watched every van. The slightest movement of a curtain often caused by the wind rather than an early-bird camper, and the boys would come running, rapping on the door, shouting: "*Baguette*! *Brot*! Bread!"

Abdullah started by gently knocking on my door at five thirty in the morning. It took several days to explain to him that I had no intention to buy any bread that early in the morning.

Finally, he understood. "Me, I wait. *Madame* open door. After, I come sell bread."

It was a deal. He would let me sleep in and protect me from other bread sellers waking me at ungodly hours and in return for this favour, I would buy my bread exclusively from him.

However, this morning he could not wait. He obviously bore gripping news and hammered on the door until I opened.

"*Madame*!" he shouted, panting like the beach dogs in the midday heat. "Salim's money! All gone! *Les voleurs*!"

Oh, my God!

"Salim had his money stolen?" I rubbed my eyes and tried to wake up.

Abdullah leant his bike against my van and sank onto the sand. "*Oui, Madame*," he continued, "Salim drink much, much wine. Then sleep, wake up and all money gone."

I sank onto the sand next to Abdullah. "Silly man," I muttered.

Salim had spent some of the money on alcohol, drank himself unconscious and became easy prey for the rest of the village. What a fool he was! I did not expect the thieves to get far though, with the police being so overly present in this country. Still, I was shocked about the news. What was Salim going to do? A man who only knew one letter of the alphabet? Whose passport expired five years ago?

"*Madame, une baguette? Deux? Trois?*"

For Abdullah, it was business as usual.

After breakfast, I drove into Agadir to visit the souk in order to buy some candles for Yassin and a pair of sturdy sandals for Nadah and me. The palm lined Boulevard Mohamed V swept me into the town, past the hotel resort on my right.

Many Moroccans are unpredictable drivers weaving in and out of lanes randomly and demonstrating a rather vague knowledge of traffic rules. The traffic on the Boulevard was particularly bad. There could have been three lanes each side in and out of town, had there been any markings. But the vast slap of dull black tarmac invited each driver to position his car wherever it suited him best. Sometimes four cars squeezed next to each other only to weave across the width of the boulevard a second later like in a gigantic game of snooker. To add to the excitement, a few donkey carriages were sprinkled in, a couple of sheep, a goat, wild dogs. People would just step onto the road in a kind of Russian roulette. It would probably make a challenging computer game.

I turned left into the city centre. There is no history in Agadir beyond forty years back when an earthquake destroyed the old medina on the hilltop and part of the new town by the sea. Dysentery, typhoid and cholera threatened to spread and within a few days the remaining part of Agadir had been bulldozed down by government machineries. The stricken population did not have enough time to recover possessions from their houses.

Nowadays, Agadir's streets are lined with whitewashed breezeblock houses in unappealing seventy's architecture; the whole town had been rebuilt.

I entered the souk through a gate in the ramparts. Although the orange-red crenulated walls with bastions and ornate gateways looked ancient and authentic, they – like the rest of Agadir- had been reconstructed. The souk is split into two parts: the colourful, scented food market and the artisan quarter, where I liked to spend hours watching shoes being made, dresses being sewn, pots being hammered into shape and ornate gates being welded.

The paths of the souk were teaming with people, many of them pasty looking tourists, huddled together in small clusters, clutching handbags and avoiding eye contact with anyone outside the group.

I strode along, as if I knew where to go. In my experience, it puts the self-appointed guides off pestering me to pay them for a guided tour. Well, sometimes it does.

"You German? English?"

I walked on, unable to shake him off in amongst the throng of people.

"Italiano?"

"I show you souk. Verrry, verrrry cheap."

I stared ahead.

"I am a student and want to learn your language."

I turned around. "No, you are mistaken. I do not need a guide. Please leave me alone."

The student smiled and stayed. I trailed him behind me like on a piece of invisible string. I dashed into rails of *djellabas* and crouched behind piles of *babouches*. Whenever I popped up to see if I had managed to "loose" him – there he was, smiling at me. I slipped into the artisan market and darted in and out of small stalls like a lunatic, throwing *bonjour* and *au revoir* at the stallholders in the same breath. The student followed and smiled.

When a large group of tourists filled the pathway and pushed us apart, I sprinted into a tiny stall and I hid behind a shelf. Through the window, I watched the student hurry past and disappear. He was no longer smiling.

"Great," I hissed, punching the air.

"Limestone," a voice said behind me.

I focussed on the little sculptures, which inhabited the dusty shelf in front of me. They were light coloured, the shape of humans, with huge sad looking heads and slumping shoulders. They touched something inside me with their aura of displacement and loneliness. Maybe I should buy one and make it happy. On the other hand, maybe it could keep me company. Maybe one of them was I. I turned round and looked into the face of a young Moroccan man.

"They are beautiful." I said.

"Thank you." The man bowed slightly. "My name is Abdul. Please have tea with me."

I sat down on a small wooden stool in the back of Abdul's shop. The tea was refreshing and I leant back against the wall, which was covered with a colourful piece of fabric. The coins sewn around the edge gave a little tinkle.

"Did you make all those?" I asked Abdul, pointing at the sculptures.

"Yes, I did. With my knife," he answered.

Abdul fetched one sculpture after the other from the shelf and handed them over to me to have a look. I liked them all. Each one had its own life story, its own secrets. I decided for a little statue, which was holding its oversized head in its hands, seemingly lost in thought and carrying the burden of the whole world on his shoulders. I named him Atlas after the Greek myths. Or, after the vast mountain range rising up behind Agadir.

"Did you really make this one?" I enquired.

"Yes, of course." He did not bash an eyelid.

For a while, we haggled over the price.

"Can you please carve your name at the bottom?" I asked. "Artists always do that."

Abdul laughed loudly, which turned into a cough. He peeled a penknife from his trouser pocket and began to scratch about clumsily. He definitely did not use his knife for anything else than cutting oranges into wedges or cleaning his fingernails.

I did not care. I liked the little statue and it did not really matter if Abdul or Mohamed or Fatima had made it. Somebody had created it, and that was all that mattered.

I paid and said good-bye, but Abdul's attention was already focussed on the next gullible customers. I watched him head for a group of shorts-clad pensioners from Europe led by a sturdy blonde hotel rep. She was holding an umbrella over her head to be visible to her herd. The pensioners were shuffling down the street in danger of missing Abdul's shop.

Within seconds, Abdul had detoured the whole group towards his shop, while the rep walked on with her umbrella as if expecting rain in the covered market and talking loudly to herself. In English.

"You've lost your sheep," I said to her, pointing at the shop before exploding with laughter.

Bo Beep's face coloured deeply red, matching the Moroccan tableware displayed behind her. She sprinted back to the shop to protect her charge from exploitation by a con-sculptor. I clutched my stomach and my little Atlas. Sniggering like a deranged woman, I ambled along looking left and right for a pair of sandals between size four and nine and some magical candles, which would lead streams of customers onto Yassin's terrace.

Somebody bumped into me. "*Excusez-moi.*"

My heart started to beat faster. I looked up and straight into a pair of green eyes.

It was Not Nick, the French man from the laundrette. My stomach contracted, my hands became clammy and my tongue turned into a dumpling. I felt like a sixteen-year-old teenager with a crush on the arts teacher.

"Oh, hi – eh - Not Nick. Fancy bumping into you, or into me, rather! Still holidaying in Agadir?" I blabbed. He must have been here for weeks.

A wide smile swept across his face.

"I was hoping to see you again," Not Nick said. "I need to tell you something."

My God, he has fallen in love with me! That's why he was still here. He had been trying to find me. Bless him – that was indeed romantic.

He bent down and whispered into my ear, "Next time you do your washing you should use washing powder. It helps enormously."

I stared at him, surrounded by pieces of shattered illusion, trying to shake off the pleasant feeling of his warm breath on my neck.

"You left something behind," he continued, beaming at me.

I squirmed with embarrassment. Oh, my God, a sock, a pair of knickers, a grey old bra. I was going to die.

Out of the depths of the pocket of his jeans, he pulled a token. A token from the launderette. The one I had not used to buy powder, but left lying on the washing machine.

Our eyes met.

"Luc!" a female voice called out. "Luc, *regarde*!"

Not Nick turned round. I followed his glance. A dark-haired Parisian looking woman smiled at us, holding up a couple of small lanterns in her *petites* hands. Neat haircut, clothes of expensive chic, loads of self-esteem. So this was his flavour! I wondered where he had met her. She was not the launderette or beach type. More likely club or casino. She was the opposite of me, the gipsy, the eternal hippy, the traveller, with a secret enthralment for fairies and folk.

"*Attende!*" Not Nick put one hand on my shoulder. "I will be back in a second!"

I used the second of his absence to disappear untraceably in the crowds.

I wanted to get back to Taghazout, crawl into Yassin's den and forget about Not Nick and the Parisian chic. Memories of pain and deceit rose up around me like walls to protect me. In passing, I snapped a pair of sturdy looking sandals the size of small fishing boats and paid the surprised stallholder the full asking price.

"But *Madame*, I can give you cheaper," he ran after me.

"No, it is alright," I shouted back, trying to put a safe distance between Not Nick and me. Or Luc. Or whatever his name was.

"Fifty percent, *Madame*," he shouted, trying to keep up with me.

I rushed on, listening to his fading lamenting. I did not feel like haggling.

In a small stall on the edge of the souk I found a torn plastic bag with dusty candle stumps. "*Combien?*" I held up the tattered bag, ready to take it at any price in my hurry to get away.

The ancient Moroccan, almost buried under his goods, waved his hands and said, "*Un cadeau.*"

The day had been full of surprises.

I was confused. I was sad. For years, I had not allowed myself to fall in love, not even to be attracted to a man. Not after what happened with Tobin. But Not Nick did not care about the walls, I had erected. He did not even care about the barbed wire and the glass on the top, the spring guns, the Rottweiler. He just crept in and shook the structure of my carefully constructed I-won't-be-hurt-again attitude.

At two o'clock, I arrived outside the little supermarket on the beach. I waited for half an hour for Yassin-who-was-also-a-builder and was about to leave, when his brother arrived.

"So, where is your brother? You told me last night he would be here at two."

"Yassin is in Tiznit and will be back in a few days, *insha'allah*."

"Salim paid me a commission of one thousand. Now his money has gone, he wants two hundred back," my friend Yassin lamented.

The sun had set and I was melting the candles onto the bottom of Yassin's precious water glasses.

"They will break," he cried.

"No, they won't," I assured him, hoping they wouldn't.

I placed one glass on each table. Immediately, the terrace was bathed in a flickering twilight. The few locals looked up at me in startled bewilderment.

"See, Yassin, with a bit of effort you can make it really nice." I looked around with content. "Soon you will be so busy, that you will have to employ extra staff."

Yassin shook his head and retreated to the security of his kitchen. While my idea was not proving a success, Yassin preferred to stay away from the scene to hide his embarrassment.

"If this doesn't do the trick I will add some napkins. Or flowers," I mumbled to myself, thinking that this was much more pleasurable than dealing with a stubborn builder.

Chapter Nine

I was taking measurements inside my four walls just to do something in terms of building and to silence the voice inside me which was nagging me to give up and look for holiday accommodation instead.

I was close to tears.

There is no privacy in Morocco, no solitude in this vast country, paradoxically, neither on top of the Atlas Mountains, nor in the Sahara Desert and certainly not in Taliouine. My neighbour Yassin and another man, whom he introduced as "Mohamed, *fils* Moulham" entered the four walls sheepishly, offered help and stood around smoking evil smelling cigarettes which made my stomach heave.

"*Madame, travail*?" my neighbour Yassin asked.

I was ashamed. Here I was indulging in self-pity, while my neighbours could hardly afford to buy the vegetables for the daily *tajine*. Yes, there was work to do, and I was suddenly propelled into activity. If I built this house, at least it could provide some employment for the village people. I shook frustration and uncertainty off with angry determination.

"*Azih*, Yassin."

He followed me outside.

Rather than squatting behind the argan trees like my neighbours, I was planning to have a toilet, the contents of which would be flushed into a soak-away by a solar-powered pump. I had no idea how this could be made to work, but was confident that it would not be too difficult to set up, even for someone like me, who has always been hopeless in science. The soak-away had to be dug into solid rock, just outside my house.

"I need a hole here, Yassin," I explained and drew a circle into the dust.

"It needs to be three metres deep and two metres wide." My arms were flying about, explaining width and depth and three metres and two metres.

My neighbour Yassin understood very quickly and offered himself for this job. We agreed that it would not take longer than ten days and that I would pay him one thousand two hundred and fifty dirham. I had no idea who was ripping off whom. The only comparison I had was the fresh water cistern in the house, which had cost Salim two thousand dirham. I might have struck a bargain there, although slight doubt crept in when I looked into Yassin's beaming face. However, I preferred to pay too much to underpaying Yassin.

As they were so eager to help, I asked Yassin and Mohamed, which way the terrace should face. Should it be this way, looking west over the Atlantic?

"*Oui, oui, Madame.*" They nodded enthusiastically.

Or should it face south towards Agadir?

"*Oui, oui, Madame.*" More passionate nodding of heads.

I realised that in order to communicate with my neighbours I had to learn Berber.

I took the path to the village square. The school was housed in a low breezeblock building with two rooms, one for the boys and one for the girls. There was a small dwelling at the far end of the square, like a miniature tower, which contained a toilet. The village children's preference was *al fresco* though, judging by the pooh-paved space behind the tower.

I stopped in the middle of the dusty square taking in the view of the surrounding hills, each one topped with a village and guarded by the mosque of Ait M'hamed. The herb-scented air was dry and warm. It was tranquil. A chorused chanting of the Koran came from the classrooms. Raza the pregnant village dog slowly crossed the square and slumped down with a grunt in the shade of the school building.

When the children's voices stopped, I approached the house and hovered indecisively in the doorway. The teacher looked at me and jumped up. Little heads turned round, with dark eyes like chocolate buttons.

I cleared my throat.

The girls nudged each other. "*Madame, Madame*," some of them whispered.

"*Bonjour*." I gave a little wave.

The teacher did not smile.

I fiddled with the hem of my shirt.

Someone sniggered.

"What can I do for you?" the teacher asked in French.

"I would like to learn Berber," I answered, letting go of the hem. "Maybe you could teach me?"

"*Je suis desole, Madame*. I can't," he answered.

"You can't?"

"No, but I can lend you books. I will bring them tomorrow."

He turned back to the class and hissed the little girls to attention.

"*Merci, Monsieur*," I murmured, leaving the classroom, feeling rejected beyond measure.

"The best way to learn the language is to learn it from the village women," he called after me.

A classroom full of shrieks and giggles marked the end of my visit.

As there was nothing left to do for me in Taliouine, I set off for the beach, where I was planning to spend a peaceful afternoon waiting for either inspiration or a builder to cross my path.

I stopped at the café.

"Yassin, why do you think, the teacher in Taliouine will not give me lessons in Berber? I would pay him for it. He did not even smile at me. I think he does not like me."

My friend spooned instant coffee into two glasses.

"It is not that," he answered, pouring hot milk over the granules.

I watched him scoop up the skin of the milk and throw it into the sink.

"What is it then?"

"Hamid is not allowed to."

"He is not allowed to? Because I am a foreigner? A woman?"

"Because it is not allowed to teach Tamazight, only French and Arabic."

"But it is the language of most people here."

Yassin pushed one of the glasses over to me.

"Yes, so most people are very angry. Here, have a coffee."

"Thanks." I reached for the sugar. "And?"

"And what?"

"Tell me more about this subject, Yassin." My friend was not a very talkative person.

"People in government say Arabic is the language of the Koran and so it should be the first language in Morocco. But the new king will change many things."

I remembered something.

"Yassin, is it not allowed to give your child a Berber name?"

"No, it is not allowed. Names have to be Arabic. The oldest son is always called Mohamed, the oldest daughter Fatima, then there is Yassin, Abdullah, Ahmed, Yasmina, Mina..."

Finally, I understood why there were so many people with the same name in this part of the world.

The beach was patrolled by a soldier, a sturdy Sadam-Hussein-look-alike, who sniffed around the camp and invited himself for cups of coffee into the various camper vans. He usually stayed too long, asking too many questions and probing too deeply into personal affairs. His *raison d'être* was to catch one of the New Age Travellers smoking hashish. Or anybody else - he was not fussed. The highest possibility for him though seemed to lie with the Hippies, as he called them.

Two weeks earlier, there had been an encounter between him and a young couple from Austria, who had come to Morocco on the plane for one week and spent the nights in a hired car on the beach. Huddling against the worn-out tyres of the battered Fiat, they had been sharing a tiny joint.

The soldier, with a nose as sensitive as truffle pig's, came galloping down the beach from behind the sand dunes, tripped over one of the homeless beach dogs and crashed down at the couples' feet. So shocked were they at the sight of the soldier dropping out of the sky and rolling in the sand like a dog in fish guts that they could do nothing but giggle and marvel at the effect of whatever they were smoking. It was certainly worth the money.

Within a split second, the soldier was back on his feet, straightened up his ragged khaki jacket and put a grimace on his face, which made the young couple choke on their sniggers.

"You smoke 'ashish," he cried out.

The young girl pressed the tiny bud into the sand.

"You know what it means in Morrrrocco?" he boomed, reducing the two to a couple of whippets exposed to the north wind.

Whatever it meant in Morocco – the gunfire of Berber he shot at them sounded like the Moroccan equivalent to deportation, prison, torture and capital punishment. The girl started to cry and hid behind her boyfriend's quivering shoulder.

After this outburst, the soldier smoothed down the sleeves of his uniform and examined his fingernails. "Maybe you have a little *cadeau* for me? Just to calm my nerves, I mean?" His voice was soft and gentle then.

The couple trembled in unison.

"It is rrreally a lovely spot for holiday." He was looking around as if seeing the beach for the first time. He was mellow, fatherly even.

71

After handing over a *cadeau* in exchange for freedom from punishment, the couple fled the beach, obviously having traded in the budget for the remaining days of their holidays.

The soldier walked off contentedly, licking his fingers and flipping through the wad of dirham he had just extracted, which no doubt would be invested in the little villa he was building up the hill in Tamraght.

Usually, I managed to escape him by sitting inside my van with my door shut pretending I had gone for a walk, but that day I did not see him approaching. He sneaked up and sat down in front of my van with a triumphant smile on his face.

"You make coffee?" He rubbed his hands together, pleased about having finally caught me out.

I made a cup of coffee and handed it to him.

"You need builder, you speak to my brrrrother," he commanded.

I kicked a stick across the path. The last thing I needed was the soldier and his family getting involved in my building project. Before I could stop him, he grabbed my cardboard model and corrected my design. He changed windows, staircases and terraces, as if it was his house.

"Leave it to my brrrrother," he bellowed. "Tomorrrrow at ten, here on the beach."

It was an order. He left surprisingly quickly, but then turned round. He came back, very slowly, very close, pointed his finger at me and said, "You live here – no guns, no drrrugs, no politics." His thick black moustache quivered.

A picture flashed through my head of myself sitting in a sparsely furnished room, a bright light shining into my face, my body wired up, and hovering above was the cruel smile of the soldier, who was about to increase the voltage.

It was a warning. How on earth could I avoid his brother?

Searching for inspiration, I wandered through Taghazout, kicking up dust and nearly choking on the stench of bacteria multiplying on the sun-baked rubbish in the dried-out riverbed. I walked past the chicken stall, listening to the screeching of a chicken-that-knows. No doubt, at sunset it would be decapitated, de-feathered and portioned into *tajine*-sized bits. A dark cloud of flies buzzed off the ground leaving behind a small pile of guts.

There was a market on the square near the bus stop. Jewellery and colourful rugs were spread out on the ground. I ambled along the rows.

"*Madame*, you buy ring?"

"Carpet, *Madame*?"

They laughed, knowing that I never bought anything as their prices were ridiculously inflated. I laughed back, grateful for being considered one up from the usual tourist.

As always, the village was a man's world. Only a few women rushed around, scarves pulled up over their mouths, clutching bags with shopping, heading back to their dwellings. Men were everywhere, talking, smoking, spitting, haggling, selling, buying, arguing, drinking coffee. Most of them seemed to have all the time in the world.

The overweight builder was slouching on the counter of his DIY stall when I walked past. He looked at me, and I found myself saying hello to him. To my surprise, he seemed to understand. He nodded and grimaced, which with a bit of imagination could have even been interpreted as a smile.

I wondered why he had been so hostile at the café. Was it really because I was a woman, or because I did not understand the language? Maybe it had to do with my friend Yassin.

I was ashamed of this thought and felt disloyal. Yassin had been my friend almost forever.

Still, a tiny doubt continued to nag, until I had an idea.

I drove to Tamraght.

The builders' merchant was by the side of the main road and occupied the ground floor of a house which has been in the progress of being built for years. As so often in Morocco, the shop had no sign, because many people could not read. For easy identification, pipes and bags of cement, wheelbarrows and rolls of cable were piled up on the dusty drive in the front.

Ahmed, who ran the shop, was a friendly man.

I had visited him before, when in my first excitement I had bought a few screwdrivers, nails and a hammer, to gradually build up a stock of tools, a woman-who-builds-a-house would need.

"I am going to build a house," I had told him with my head held high and my shoulders stretched back.

He had sold me, what I had asked for, and his eyes had sparkled.

"*Ah, bonjour Madame*," he greeted me from behind his counter, stretching out his hand to shake mine. "*Ca va*? What do we need today? A couple of screws? Maybe five bricks and a tiny bag of cement for the new house?"

"I need your help." I ignored his attempt to tease me.

Yassin-the-builder arrived ten minutes after Ahmed had phoned him.

Half an hour later, we had drawn up a simple plan of nine steps. It was playschool level, and Yassin-the-builder understood.

1. build internal walls on the ground floor
2. build staircase to first floor
3. build roof, which is also floor of the first floor
4. build walls for one room on the first floor, which should take half of the floor space
5. build a brick wall, 1.50 metres high, around the remaining floor space to create a terrace.
6. build a roof on the first floor room
7. built a brick wall around the roof, to create roof terrace with 360 degree view
8. build staircase from first floor terrace to roof terrace
9. plaster inside, outside, put in windows and doors

Ahmed produced an almost childlike drawing for Yassin-the-builder.

"*D'accord*?" I turned to the builder. I could have slapped him on his back I was so relieved.

He grunted and shifted his weight from one leg to the other. "It will be alright," Ahmed said. "Yassin is a good builder. He knows what you want now, and he will do it."

I wished I had the same confidence in Yassin's goodwill.

We agreed a price. Half of the sum was payable in advance and the rest on completion as it was custom in Morocco. There were not going to be any contracts. I had to take his word that he would do what we had just agreed, *insha'allah*, and that in two weeks the work would be finished, *insha'allah*.

"This is how it works in Morocco," Ahmed said. "Think about it and then let me know. Yassin can start straight away. Now, is there anything you want to buy?"

"Yes, I'd like a couple of screws and five bricks please. Oh – and a tiny bag of cement. For my new house."

How was I going to get rid of the soldier's brother?

Chapter Ten

The problem with the soldier's brother was easily dealt with. He had not arrived by ten o'clock. Two minutes past ten, I left the beach and went up to Taliouine to view the progress of my soak-away.

It was coming on nicely. Piles of earth and rocks in front of my door showed that the hole was being dug. Yassin-my-neighbour was sitting on the edge, smoking one of his stinking cigarettes. Jalal piled up small stones around his father's feet.

"*Bonjour*, Yassin."

"*Bonjour, Madame*."

When I leant over the edge, I saw pregnant Mina at the bottom hammering and hacking away at the rocks. She smiled and waved when she saw me. I looked at Yassin, who was smiling too.

"Yassin, Mina is pregnant," I said sternly, painting a little protruding tummy with my hands.

"*Oui, oui,*" he answered proudly and continued to smoke.

I knew from fragments of our conversations that Yassin was a man of leisure, very much in tune with the pleasant side of life like birdsong, peacefulness, cigarettes and lazing about. Mina's approach to life was more practical. Yassin's hedonistic streak left them often with nothing to eat, and so she usually pestered him to find work until he could not stand it any longer.

77

He then would go out and find a job, make Mina do the work and life was peaceful once again.

I disapproved but what could I do? Yassin's job seemed to be lifting Mina into the hole in the morning and out in the evening to prepare a meal.

Nashiema appeared outside her house; her son Samir was bobbing up and down on her hip.

"*La bes,* Nashiema, *bejer.*"

"*Bejer, Madame, la bes.*" Nashiema smiled, her head slightly bent. She had black straight hair like most Berber women, but hers was as dark as a moonless night. Her skin was the colour of ripe dates. Her face was perfectly proportioned, with high cheekbones and a straight nose. Her slanted brown eyes were most expressive, sparkling, teasing, alert. Even with Samir's weight on her hip, she stood upright with her head held high. She was like a princess amongst the village people.

"*Madame* – henna?" Nashiema asked, pointing at my hands and feet.

I still wished my neighbours would take to calling me by my first name.

"Henna, *Madame*?" Nashiema asked again.

"Yes, I'd love to," I answered.

"*Zig sbah?*"

Today? Why not? I had taken the first hurdle of my building project and a little pampering was called for.

"*Eyeh,*" I agreed.

"*Azih, Madame!*" Nashiema waved and headed for her house.

Like in Yassin's house, the brightly painted metal door led into a tiny courtyard, the only difference being that Nashiema's house was very recent. A small part of the breezeblock wall was whitewashed; the rest stared at me in gloomy grey. On the top of the wall, metal rods stretched into the sky waiting for the day when there would be enough money to add a floor.

A gas bottle sat on the scrubbed concrete ground next to Nashiema's modest collection of kitchen tools: one bowl, three glasses, a battered kettle and the traditional *tajine* dish made from clay. Samir's doll-sized garments were spread out on the floor to dry. It was spotlessly clean.

The only doorway off the yard led into the only room. A mattress on the floor covered with a yellow reddish woven blanket served as bed and sofa. Nadah was sitting on the edge of the mattress, greeting me with a bright smile.

"*Madame! La bes!*" she exclaimed and jumped up.

"*Bonjour, Nadah.*"

I shed my shoes and entered.

Nadah rushed past me and slipped into my discarded sandals. Humming to herself, she promenaded around the courtyard. Then she took Samir from Nashiema, swung him onto her solid hips, winked at me and left. With our sandals. I was pleased with this acquisition. They were slightly too big for me, but a much better fit for Nadah.

We decided to henna my feet. Nashiema brought a bowl with water, soap and a towel and indicated me to wash my feet. Meanwhile she was rushing about collecting various utensils.

After washing my feet, I sank onto the mattress and watched Nashiema prepare the henna paste.

She poured the green powder onto a battered metal plate and mixed it with cellulose from a large brown glass bottle. A sharp scent like nail varnish emerged from the plate.

Nashiema spread four stencils out in front of me.

"*Choisir, Madame,*" Her fingers touched each stencil.

I picked a garland of filigree flowers.

Nashiema smiled. "*Ifulki,*" she said, her thumb and finger forming a circle of approval.

She cut a lemon in half and, with her knife, emptied the juice onto the dark green henna mash. Using her hands, she mixed it into a thick paste adding a little water from time to time. An earthy scent emitted from the plate, like spinach, mixing pleasantly with the smell of lemon still lingering in the air. Nashiema's hands were starting to look orange. She covered the plate with a cloth and pushed it aside, then laid the stencils along the sides of my feet and across the toes and held them in place with black tape. Her fingers were cool on my skin.

"Nadah – Philippe – *mariage*?" I tried in French.

Nashiema, who was covering the top of my foot with tape, so the henna would not stain the skin, nodded. She crossed her fingers for good luck and grinned.

"Where is Philippe?" I asked, turning the inside of my hand up in question.

"Philippe? *France*." Nashiema slapped a handful of green paste onto the sole of my foot and started smoothing it down with her fingers. "Visa Nadah."

So, that was the story. Philippe had gone to France, hopefully to sort out Nadah's papers. I tried very hard not be prejudiced, but could not help imagining Philippe as a small dull oldish man, who was prepared to trap an innocent maiden from the mountains into a cheerless marriage. Who then could not make up his mind and kept stringing her along. Maybe I would be able to talk to him one day and tell him what I thought about that kind of behaviour.

Nashiema's hands, already dyed dark orange, were sculpturing the paste around my foot, with fluent and experienced movements, dipping in and out of lemony water. In the end, my feet resembled two smooth, slightly deformed watermelons which Nashiema carefully stuck into two plastic bags before covering them with a blanket.

A wave of heat rushed through my body. I have never been good at this type of thing. In my younger years, when hairdressers applied highlights by covering the head tightly with a plastic cap, pulling out thin strands of hair with a crocheting needle and plastering them with a bleaching agent, I was known for jumping out of the chair with a scream and pulling the cap off my head. This would result in bleach being spread randomly over my hair, and instead of fashionably streaked I would look like a patchwork quilt.

Would I be able to remain like this for hours? Or would I suddenly have to tear the bags off my feet like someone who cannot breathe? Leaving orange footprints all over Nashiema's floor whilst running for fresh air?

Nashiema indicated me to lie back. She stuffed a cushion behind my back and propped up my feet, slowly, as not move the stencils. She pulled a woollen blanket out of the cupboard and tucked me in. I breathed deeply in and out. The room was warm. I felt pampered and swaddled. *Spa Nashiema*, I thought sleepily, we could turn it into a business...

Before I could drift off, the door opened and the house filled with chirping and laughter. In small groups, the *Mesdames* and *Mademoiselles* of Taliouine entered Nashiema's room, leaving a pile of orphaned sandals by the doorstep. I had not realised that the henna session would bear entertainment for the female members of the village. The smell of cooking and coriander clung to their colourful dresses as well as the sweet spicy scent of perfume, feminine and different to the male smell of Taghazout. The women had come to take a close look at the crazy foreign *Madame* who for once could not escape their curiosity, because she was trapped on the mattress with her legs in the air.

Nashiema introduced me to a succession of Cherifas, Fatimas and Minas, who all shook my hand with a grin and a *"La bes, Madame"*. Some of them could not stop giggling. Then they sat down on the stone floor, chattering and tittering with high-pitched voices which seemed to belong to exotic birds rather than sturdy mountain women. They folded their legs into comfortable positions, and I noticed even under the longest and thickest skirt an ankle-length pair of leggings. The older women wore socks and did not expose an inch of flesh. Others had beautiful henna patterns on their feet in various states of fading. Their garments were a jumble of skirts, dresses, topped with blouses, jumpers, sweatshirts, often in ill-fitting sizes, cleverly held up and together by bits of fabric or old discarded scarves. All colours and patterns were combined in a random fashion, probably insulting the European dress sense, but here in Morocco it created a startling colourfulness, especially against the backdrop of the faded countryside.

I was sweating, and my immobile feet gave me the most curious sensations. At times, the henna seemed to be burning holes into my skin.

A meagre chicken ran in and out of the room, clucking loudly.

I liked the way the headscarves were draped over the women's heads, leaving the faces and a great part of their hair uncovered. The ends were tied to a bow on top of the head and left to stand up like an extra set of ears.

"*Ifulki*." I said and pointed at the nearest headscarf, a bright indigo blue affair.

The chirping stopped, and after a mortifying second of stillness giggles erupted. Was it my pronunciation?

The woman, whose scarf I had pointed at, laughed and pulled it off; shiny henna-tinted hair cascaded down her back. She crawled over to the mattress and tied the scarf around my head. A musky scent lingered around my nose and reminded me of patchouli incense stick. I felt for the bow on the top and it was there. I was satisfied and so were the women, who were clapping their hands and cheering.

I enjoyed getting to know my new neighbours, listening to their relentless fast-paced conversations in Berber staccato and to the cheerful songs into which they broke from time to time. I tried to communicate, but it was nearly impossible. Still, I was part of the group, just by being there. It seemed as if I was not expected to contribute anything else but my presence. For several hours, I was trapped in this ungainly position, leaving my feet feeling too hot and almost without blood circulation. Nashiema made tea and served flat bread, which had to be dipped into soft rancid butter first and then into honey, until it was dripping with delicious sweetness.

After a few hours I lost the feeling of having any feet. I panicked. My feet had gone, merged into a green smelly paste. Childhood memories flashed through my brain, of holidays in Italy, of squashed watermelons on the road after falling off a lorry. I had the overwhelming urge to jump up and shifted uncomfortably. My bottom felt sore.

Several times, Nashiema checked the dying process by opening up the layers and scraping away a tiny bit of henna, on which occasions I could see my feet where still there.

Finally, it was over.

The women hauled themselves up from the floor and adjusted skirts and headscarves. Each one shook my hand, said "*beslama*" and the colourful bunch filed out of the room. They rummaged through the pile of shoes for the right pairs and left the house.

The blankets were lifted off my feet. Despite the heat in the room, I felt cold. Nashiema cut the plastic bags open. It was time. I was itching to give my feet a good scratch. The strong smell of spinach left in a dish on a sun-drenched windowsill hit my nostrils. With a blunt knife, Nashiema peeled some of the green paste off, then slowly tore away the stencils and continued scraping as much Henna off as possible. She told me not to use water until the next day.

"*Demain*," she said, pointing at a bowl of water.

My feet were sporting bright orange flowery garlands, which within the next few days would turn black. I found it most beautiful.

"Are you married, Nashiema?"

Nashiema looked up.

"Mohamed," she said with a level voice.

She smiled and jumped up. Out of the drawer in her cupboard, Nashiema took a fake golden plastic chain and put it round my neck. Touched by her kindness I gave her a hug and insisted on paying for the henna.

"*Ifulki, mezyan, shokran, wacha.*" Thank you, thank you and thank you.

It was going to be dark soon, and I was eager to get down to Taghazout. My friend Yassin's warning about bandits lurking in the bushes disquieted me slightly. My sandals were back from their excursion. I slipped them on and left Nashiema's little house.

"*Beslama.*" Nashiema waved after me.

I was still wearing the indigo blue headscarf.

83

My neighbour Yassin had already lifted Mina out of the hole and probably sent her home to make supper. He was sitting on a rock, looking out for the sunset. I left him the key for my cistern in case he needed water for the soak away.

"*Bonne nuit*, Yassin."

"*Bonne nuit, Madame*."

I walked swiftly down the hill.

Feeling the warm evening air on my face, I changed my mind. I felt brave and not at all like going back to Taghazout immediately. I decided to take a detour and visit the village of Ait Tabbia on the neighbouring hilltop. Bandits! In the hills of Taghazout? Lying in waiting, because the only tourist in the mountain world might make her way down after dark? With the monetary equivalent of three round breads in her pocket?

My friend Yassin was sometimes overanxious.

Chapter Eleven

I walked downhill and crossed the new road. A stony path led past small fields and climbed up the hill to the village of Ait Tabbia. Similar to Taliouine, it perched on the hilltop: a collection of flat-roofed one-storey dwellings and a sprinkling of date palms. The sky was already colouring and the peacefulness of a day fulfilled was hovering above.

"Hello," a voice called out to me in English. A man appeared from behind a dilapidated stone house.

I recognised him immediately. I had seen him before, through a hole in my decaying breezeblock wall, when he was leading a herd of English tourists around our mediaeval village.

I stopped. "Hello, how are you?"

"Thank you, very well," he said, rolling the 'r'. He strode towards me and stretched out his hand. "My name is Lahcen. You bought Salim's house?"

There were no secrets in this part of the world.

"I did," I answered and followed his invitation to sit down on the broken wall. "And you are making me a tourist attraction."

He laughed. I looked around and realised that he was renovating the house behind the wall, which must have been deserted decades ago. Lahcen followed my glance.

"It is old house of my family," he explained proudly.

"Where did you learn English?" I asked.

"From my father. And work with tourists." He turned to me. "Why do you want to build house in Arabic country? Is very difficult. Many *baksheesh*, workers are lazy and police is everywhere. You should come here for holiday and rent a room or house. Much better."

"What do you do with tourists, take them for a walk?" I did not want to hear about the difficulties I was probably going to have to face.

Lahcen jumped off the wall. He was about my age, slightly taller than I am, with the tanned weather-beaten complexion of someone living and working outdoors. His hair was curly and nearly touched his shoulders. A Jack-Sparrow-look-alike. The pirate of Ait Tabbia.

"Come with me. I will show you." he said and set off up the hill.

I followed him.

On top of the hill stood a low whitewashed building, a rectangle of windowless walls, only interrupted by a bright blue metal door the colour of the sky. The door was decorated with heart-shaped patterns in white and yellow. Coloured pieces of broken tiles were forming small mosaics on the wall.

Lahcen opened the door. We stepped into a vast courtyard. On the stone floor, there was an arranged chaos of plants in pots – bougainvillea, geraniums, ferns and palms. The faint tinkle of a fountain reached my ear; I spotted a mossy stone basin, half hidden by bushes of papyrus. The centrepiece of the yard was a rectangular wrought iron table with eight matching chairs. Most fascinating of all was a selection of fossils leaning up against the wall. I ran my hand over the shiny smooth surface of a dinner-plate-sized shell. It was perfectly preserved.

"Where do those come from?" I asked.

Lahcen shrugged his shoulders and gave a curt wave. "You can find them everywhere here. Come on; let me show you the rooms."

In true Berber fashion, several doors led off the yard into several rooms which were fed on light and air through the doorways and windows opening into the courtyard. There were no windows in the outside walls. I walked from bedroom to bedroom, from kitchen to sitting room. It was a rather European concept, but then, it was not. It was a balanced mixture of the two different cultures. Somebody had furnished and decorated the house very tastefully and restored all the traditional features of a Berber habitation. If I could end up with a house a fraction as beautiful as this one, I would be happy.

"Is this your house?"

"No," Lahcen said. "It belongs to my girlfriend and her brother, Florence and Philippe. We run a business together in Taghazout: trekking with tourists in the Atlas Mountains. We take them around the villages to see real Berber life, let them stay in this house, and so on."

"Philippe? Are we talking about Philippe who is going to marry Nadah from Taliouine?"

Lahcen laughed.

"If Cherifa got her way, yes."

So, here was another part of the story. The mysterious Philippe ran a trekking business from Taghazout into the hills. He was also the co-owner of this beautiful Berber house. Maybe he was not as dull and oldish as I thought. On one of his numerous *randonnes*, he had fallen in love with Nadah. I did not put it past Cherifa to have her hands in this, to have whisked together a few aphrodisiacal mountain herbs and spiked Philippe's mint tea in order to marry her daughter from the shelf to a rich European man. The herbal power of the old Berber women should not be underestimated, my friend Yassin always told me. Anyway, there was the understanding at least from Cherifa's side that there was going to be a marriage between Philippe and Nadah at some point.

"Their business is working well. They built a beautiful house. Why do you advise me against building my house?" I asked.

Lahcen shrugged his shoulders.

"They were lucky," he said. "Times have changed."

87

After a night of tossing and turning over Lahcen's open discouragement I returned to Taliouine in search of an answer, a sign, which would help me decide what to do.

The village appeared unusually colourful. The washing had been done everywhere and the bushes were laden with garments spread out to dry in the sun. The scent of washing powder lingered in the mountain world, alien, just like me. Was this a sign? However, I was glad the old water from my cistern had saved the women from having to walk five miles to the next well.

My neighbour Yassin rushed towards me, which was an uncommonly energetic activity for a man of his kind.

"*Madame*," he shouted excitedly and pointed down the hill. "*Shuf, shuf!*"

I followed his outstretched arm until I saw what was causing his tremendous excitement. Further down the hill, ugly concrete masts had appeared out of nowhere and were growing in numbers at rapid speed. Electricity had arrived. My heart sank. Already. One could not even rely on *Insha'allah*. Allah must have approved of the plans to wire up the mountain world quicker than I had hoped. Soon, thick black wires would be cutting across my beautiful views. Radios and television sets would blare day and night, and artificial light would blind out the moon and the stars. My little dream of peacefulness and a natural live was destroyed before it had even started.

'Give up,' a voice inside me said. 'The builder is unacceptable in behaviour, everything is going to change with electricity and probably very soon the so far forgotten beach down there will be sporting several holiday resorts and artificial marinas. The area will be crawling with disagreeable noisy tourists.'

What was I doing here?

Had I lost all my senses?

Miserably I walked back to Taghazout.

Another sleepless night followed. I tried to read the signs. I made lists with pros and cons. I tried to rationalise. When the first shimmer of the day lit the mountains, I gave up. There was no rational approach to solve this problem. It was purely an emotional matter. I felt that my journey had come to an end. I was not running away anymore. I could still feel the pain of the past, of a marriage breaking down, of abuse and escape. But it had started to fade. I had moved on.

I was happy in Morocco, despite the difficulties. I had friends here. I was starting to be intrigued by my neighbours. I loved with this place, whatever happened to it. I loved the colours: the pink of the rising sun against the light blue sky, the fiery orange in the evening, the pale golden beach, the ever-changing colour of the sea - a picture book blue on a fine day and dark green and mysterious, when a storm blew across. The whitewashed houses reflected all those natural colours. The scents of spices, herbs, baking sun and stables, henna and incense-like sweetness were like perfume. The warmth of the sun was like a hug. People were forever chatting, arguing or singing, yet a few steps away, there was silence, tranquillity, only interrupted by the thunder of the ocean or the bleating of a stray goat. I was getting tired of weighing advantages against disadvantages. All those sleepless nights were starting to wear me down.

It was time for a new beginning.

After breakfast, I drove to Agadir. I withdrew a paper bag full of dirham and returned to Taghazout. I handed the money over to the slouching builder, who nearly slipped off his counter at the sight of it and even gave me a receipt in return. I felt light and pleased, and skipped along the beach, twirling around with outstretched arms, ignoring the sniggering fishermen.

"I have done it, Yassin." I stormed onto the terrace of his restaurant.

My friend Yassin had just finished the lunchtime business and was clearing away the last dirty dishes. "The police found Salim's money."

I stopped dead. "They did? Already? What happened?"

Yassin slapped his cloth at the flies, which were fighting for a crumb on the table. "He drank too much wine. Then he fell asleep. When he woke up three youths had stolen the money. You can't hide so much money in a village like Taghazout and so the police found out quickly."

"Where is the money now?"

"The police have got it. It will go to the court."

I knew what this meant. Salim would have to fill in stacks of forms – how do illiterate people manage? – and wait for a court judgement to get the money back. By the time the court makes a decision which can take any imaginable length of time, many people will have helped themselves to a little *baksheesh*, a little crumb of Salim's money cake.

"What is going to happen to the thieves?" I asked.

"Hotel Inezgane," Yassin said with a curt wave of his hand southwards.

"Hotel Inezgane? Are you sure? That doesn't sound too bad to me."

"It is not a hotel. It is a prison. And it is not good. I had a German girlfriend once. Police took her there. She had hashish in her bag. Is very, very bad." Yassin shook his head.

"Hotel Inezgane" was a feared prison south of Agadir in a village of the same name, he explained, but I was much more interested in the rare revelation of details of Yassin's wild youth.

"Your German girlfriend, Yassin? Tell me more," I demanded, moving closer.

Yassin has always had a tendency to selective hearing.

"They will be let out again, for five thousand dirham," he continued.

"That is a lot. Who could pay so much money for them?" I wondered.

"The families. I know them. It is very hard."

"What about this girlfriend?" I said, trying to revive the subject.

"Aah – is long ago," he grinned. "Now I have to go down to the beach and gut fish for the evening and you cannot come with me because you would ask all afternoon about my girlfriend and I don't want to talk."

With this, he grabbed his bucket full of fish and a sharp knife and set off.

"Please yourself," I called after him, rather huffed. "I don't want to know about your seedy past with female prisoners."

He turned round and laughed.

"Come for *tajine* tonight and tell me about your day!"

Chapter Twelve

My friend Yassin accompanied me to Taliouine the next day.
The sun was hot. By the time we had climbed the steep track
leading up to the village I was panting. Yassin drained his water
bottle.

"Look at that." I grinned, pointing towards my house.

"I told you." Yassin said.

Yassin-the-builder had not wasted time. Bricks had been
delivered and piled up toddler-style into a hut, with a piece of
cardboard for a roof.

"Oh no, Yassin!"

"They need a hut. One of workers will sleep here because
of thieves in the night. If nobody is here" – he flicked his hand –
"thieves will take everything."

"Yes, I know, but it is sitting on the *farine*. Cherifa will be
furious."

The *farine* was the place where the women made flour after
harvesting the small fields which were dotted around the village.
It was a level terrain with huge boulders dug into the ground,
only leaving a shiny surface visible, on which the corn was
crushed and ground into flour. The *farine* was in front of my
house, across the narrow dust path.

It was Cherifa's property and she was very protective of it.
There was not much flour making in Taliouine nowadays and

most families had to buy flour in Taghazout. There were not enough fields to cater for the growing population. By now I knew enough about Cherifa to assume that she was hoping to sell this napkin of land to some gullible foreigner one day: a prime location with unobstructed views.

I could see the fragile foundations of a budding friendship with my neighbour shatter. Cherifa would be putting spells on me and shooting arrows from her steely eyes.

"Don't worry. The builder has probably given her money. You must not let her intimidate you. She is only an old woman." Yassin kicked a stone across the path, hands buried in his pockets.

A metal door swung open with a squeak and banged against a stonewall. I turned to see Cherifa in the doorway of her house, arms folded in front of her chest.

"*Bonjour, Madame,*" I called.

"*Bonjour. La bes,*" she said and stared at me.

When her glance fell on my friend Yassin, he shifted from one leg to the other.

"Yassin!" she hissed and indicated him with a nod of her head to follow her into her house which he did: his shoulders slumped, his head hung like a lamb called to its slaughter.

It made me laugh. "Don't be afraid, Yassin." I called after him.

I peeped inside what was going to be my house and saw that a pillar had been erected in the middle. It seemed as if Yassin-the-builder had decided to leave the rickety outside walls Salim had built.

An ancient moped came huffing and puffing up the track, followed by a cluster of shrieking children. It came to a stop next to me.

A small man dismounted, arranged the moped on its feeble stand and stretched his hand out towards me. A toothless smile spread across his ancient wrinkled face, which was tanned by decades of outdoor work. A pair of black eyes twinkled. Pointy ears were sticking out under a GAP baseball cap. I shook his little hand.

"Moulham," the impish creature introduced itself.

Moulham was Cherifa's brother-in-law. Thanks to my friend Yassin, I was well informed about the family relations in the village. Most of the time, Cherifa and Moulham were archenemies, and their enmity split the whole village into two parties. While Cherifa's clan lived on my right side, Moulham's cluster of dwellings, which housed several sons and their families, was on my left, leaving my house and the locked-up one next to mine the front line for their war.

The children bunched around us, pulling my clothes with dirty hands. Dusty little faces looked up, streams of green snot oozing out of their noses.

"*Madame, Madame, un cadeau, bonbon, dirham.*"

"*Sir fhalek!*" Moulham hissed and the children moved swiftly to the edge of the field.

Moulham pointed at a small strip of land, adjoining my unknown neighbour's property to my left.

"*C'est a moi. Voulez-vous achetez?*"

I was surprised to be offered the handkerchief-sized plot, which was separated from my house by the narrow path, leading up to Yasmina's house, one of Cherifa's daughters. What would I do with it?

Moulham had some ideas at hand. He jumped up and down on the little piece of land, drawing imaginary walls and ceilings, telling me to make *un parking* or a garden or even build a garage with a room above. Dancing around on *le parking*, he reminded me of Rumpelstiltskin.

Two little girls started to empty their noses into the hem of their dresses.

"*Oho, shokran,*" I declined. I did not need any outbuildings.

Moulham shrugged his childlike shoulders and smiled.

"*Après, insha'allah!*" he said, grinned and pushed his moped up the path to his house, followed by the children like the Pied Piper.

My friend Yassin returned from Cherifa's house, and we left to walk back to Taghazout.

"Was she angry about the *farine*?"

We stumbled down the hill, slipping on the rocky path.

"No, the builder pays her. She is angry because you don't give more work to her son Yassin. She is no good. She is a witch. Be careful!"

"Yassin, there are no witches. What harm could she do?"

"I told you before. She is old woman from mountains. Knows many spells. She uses herbs and makes poison. Then she puts it on a cloth, touches you and you are sick. *Khaib.*" Clearly upset, he staggered through his English grammar.

"I can't believe it; are you trying to frighten me?" I laughed.

"I warn you. I went to her house one day. There was a little fire in the corner. Funny smell. I had headache for two weeks."

I shook my head. In shortest time, Cherifa had advanced from 'only an old woman' to the "wicked witch of the west".

"Yassin, you are exaggerating."

Yassin did not listen. "Never let her touch you, never look into her eyes."

Silently we walked on. Maybe there was some truth in what he was saying. Who was I to dismiss it as an old wives' tale?

"Yassin-the-builder charges tourists much more money than Moroccans. And you can't trust him," Yassin said after a while.

I stopped dead.

"What are you talking about, Yassin? You are the one who recommended the builder to me."

"With you, he is different." Yassin had picked up a stick and looked at it with great interest.

"Look into my eyes," I said, snatching the stick away. "Tell me: how can you do that? How can you set me up with someone I can't trust? I thought you were my friend."

"I am your friend," he cried. "I said, with you, he is different."

I stomped off towards Taghazout, sending little avalanches of pebbles, fossils and goat dung down the hill. Why would he be different with me?

"He must have paid you a fat commission for picking up yet another gullible stranger to rip off," I shouted back.

We had reached Taghazout. I left Yassin in a huff and headed for the beach.

Not much later Yassin found me sitting on the rocks, hurling pebbles into the water.

"I made *calamar* for you." His hands buried in his trouser pockets, he loitered beside me.

Yassin always made *calamar* for me when he wanted to make up for something, because he knew I could not resist a plate of freshly grilled seafood.

My stomach was a pushover, easily seduced and forgiving.

"What are we waiting for?" I looked at him and smiled.

It was impossible to be angry with him for long, but I felt sad as if I had woken up from a dream, in which Yassin and I were best friends forever and ever.

Chapter Thirteen

On my arrival in Taliouine the next day, I found the building site teeming with activity. I saw the shuttering going up and watched the pouring of concrete. About fifteen workers, as busy as ants, were bustling back and forth, whistling, singing and enjoying themselves.

"*Madame*! Get camera," they shouted, waving with an assortment of tools.

Several days went by, and the house was progressing steadily. I started to relax. Congratulating myself for having chosen the right builder, I entered the building site one gorgeous sunny morning, only to find that the hole for the staircase to the first floor was in the wrong place.

There was no point in arguing with Yassin-the-builder. Firstly, he was not there, secondly, he would not understand and thirdly, the damage was done. All I could do was to sit down and spend a couple of hours changing my plans around this unexpected development. I wondered what Yassin-the-builder had done with the plan Ahmed had drawn. Maybe he had used it to light the fire for his *tajine*.

The workers were going to start on the first floor. Half of the floor space was to become a room and the other half would be a spacious south-facing terrace. I had planned a staircase in the far corner leading up to the roof of the room to yet another terrace. The side and back walls of the first floor room were going to be built first, followed by the wall around the terrace. Six men were working, supervised by Yassin-the-builder's brother in the manner of a slave driver.

Also seemingly unable to speak French, the brother indicated that the water lorry had been up and filled my cistern. He was asking me for two hundred dirham, which he had paid to the lorry driver.

"Two hundred? You are joking. The price of water is 120 dirham."

I didn't know why I paid him the two hundred. Maybe I feared that Yassin-the-builder and his brother would stop the building work altogether if I annoyed them. Or forget to leave holes for the windows. Or take ten years to finish the house.

I realised that in order to stay in control I needed to be on site from dawn to dusk. I needed to bring my van up and spend the nights on the edge of the village.

At lunchtime, the builder's brother climbed onto his moped to go down to Taghazout.

"*Monsieur, Monsieur*!" I shouted against the chugging noise of his ancient two-stroke.

The builder's brother glanced at me.

"Coca Cola, *Monsieur, s'il vous plait*." I held up five fingers. "Five bottles. For the workers."

I fished a note out of my pocket. He snapped it from my hand, without taking his eyes off mine.

Two hours later he held out one hand to me, indicating "five" with the other hand.

"I gave you money already. Why do you want five more dirham?"

We stared at each other unable to understand.

"*Pour l'essence! Pour faire le course*." Moulham strolled past and patted my shoulder.

Five dirham for petrol, because I had asked him to buy five bottles of coke for his workers, when he was going to Taghazout anyway!

This was getting out of hand.

If I bought Moulham's small strip of land and turned it into *un parking* I could install my van on it as a kind of site office.

And if one day, Yasmina sold her footpath to me, the parking would be joined to my house and I could turn the whole land into a garden...

"Do you think I should buy Moulham's piece of land, Yassin?"

We were sitting on the terrace of his restaurant, which was suffused in flickering candle light, but lacking any customers while the "Copacabana" was as busy as ever.

"He wants too much money."

I nearly dropped the tea glass.

"How do you know?"

"He told me."

"And why don't I know about it? Why did you not tell me?"

"He wants too much money," Yassin repeated. "Moulham is greedy. There will be no deal."

"But we could try to bring the price down."

Yassin shrugged his shoulders. "You can try. I cannot help."

Silently we drank our tea.

"Where are all your customers, Yassin, by the way?" I detected glee in my voice, and the kind of you-hurt-me-now-I-will-hurt-you-attitude made me ashamed.

He nodded curtly towards the teaming terrace of the French café.

"I will bring some napkins and flowers. Just wait." Yassin was my friend and I was going to help him.

Yassin only looked at me.

A week later I was sitting on the ground of *le parking*, leaning back against the wall of my unknown neighbour's house, trying to work out how many kilometres I was to able follow the coastline south with my eyes, before it faded away. Forty probably. I squinted. Fifty maybe.

Le Parking was mine now, and my mind went back to the day I bought it.

One morning, Moulham had appeared with a young man in tow, whom he introduced as Mohamed, Nashiema's husband.

It was the first time I saw Mohamed. He was a dark handsome man, but his eyes were darting around, unwilling to focus and his hands were fiddling constantly with a cigarette lighter. I wondered where he spent his time, when he was not undertaking one of his fleeting visits to see his wife and his son. Nobody spoke much about him. All I knew was that he was Arabic, not Berber. Reflecting the history of Morocco, when the Berber, the original inhabitants of Morocco where driven back into the mountains in defeat by the Arabs, they were still not overly welcome in the Berber mountain community.

For Moulham to bring Mohamed along as a translator seemed odd to me, as additional to their different cultural backgrounds they belonged to opposite parties of the family at war.

"Moulham wants six thousand and six hundred for the land," Mohamed said.

I laughed and shook my head. My friend Yassin had been right; it was a crazy price. "For this amount of dirham I can buy a whole house," I said.

"Moulham is not speaking of dirham."

"No? What is he speaking of?"

"It is the old Berber money. Old men talk old money."

It was difficult to gasp the mysterious ways money was communicated in this country.

"How many dirham are we talking about?"

"Three thousand six hundred."

"I will not pay more than three thousand for the land," I told Mohamed to cut it short.

Mohamed and Moulham stuck their heads together.

"Moulham agrees to the price. Three thousand dirham for the land."

"Great. Let's go to the *notaire*." I jumped up. That had been a quick deal.

"But when you build a garage or a parking, how will you get your car in and out?"

"I know it is narrow, but don't worry. I will back onto the field opposite…"

"It is Moulham's field," Mohamed interrupted.

Moulham smiled.

"Right," I said and sat down again. "How much?"

"Moulham will sell you the corner of his field for six hundred dirham. Then you will have no problem."

Moulham nodded.

I would not be able to access *le parking* without backing into Moulham's field and it was clear to me that a never-ending neighbourly dispute over this matter would arise. I could imagine Moulham standing next to his field with his hand outstretched for toll payments every time I moved the van.

"Ok, three thousand and six hundred dirham for the lot."

Once again, I found myself seated in Monsieur Abderrahim's office, this time accompanied by Moulham. It was the same procedure as last time. Mr Abderrahim checked the papers, locked my money into the draw and set up a contract. Moulham and I signed it and left for the town hall to have our signatures certified.

So here I was, buying plot after plot like a small-scale property developer: Twenty-two square metres here (garage), eight square metres there (field), maybe soon another twenty square metres (Yasmina's path).

"*Madame*." The tiny clerk acknowledged me and bent his head back over a book the size of a breakfast tray, into which he recorded meticulously the buying and selling of properties around Taghazout. The scraping of his pen echoed across the cool marbled hall.

"*Les timbres, Madame?*"

Again, I was sent across the traffic-ridden main road to buy stamps. "*Combien?*" I sighed.

The clerk looked at his papers for a long time. *"Dix huit."*

Here we go again, I thought. It is not only the legacy of French bureaucracy. It is its combination with Morocco's attitude of *insha'allah*. Everything is vague, no commitment, no concrete information.

Eighteen? Did it mean three stamps at six dirham? Or nine at two? Or two at nine? One at eighteen, perhaps? Eighteen at one? I sniggered helplessly. The clerk had disappeared into the book again, scraping at the pages. I dashed across the road to the kiosk and bought three stamps for six dirham each.

"Non, non!" exclaimed the clerk on my return, wringing his small hands in despair.

3 x 20 dirham, he wrote on a piece of paper.

What a country this was! Was this a kind of black-humour past-time, sending hapless foreigners across the busy road a few times, possibly taking bets if he or she was run over by the speeding bus to Casablanca?

I returned to the kiosk.

"Twenty dirham? No, I don't have any. Try the telephone kiosk. "

The man in the telephone kiosk sent me to the post office, the woman in the post office sent me to Aourir, where I would find a twenty-dirham stamp, *insha'allah*.

I drove to Aourir at lightning speed, raced up and down the village and found a stationary stall, whose owner after a long search unearthed three dusty twenty-dirham stamps.

"Sixty five dirham, *Madame*, *si'l vous plait*."

"Why do you charge me five dirham more?" I knew the answer already.

"Madame, I spent a long time looking. For you. I could have served many customers in same time."

Still, it was less hassle than going all the way to Agadir. I forced a smile onto my face and paid for the stamps and his loss of earnings, then rushed back to Taghazout. Proudly waving the three stamps I ran up the steps to the entrance of the town hall only to find the door locked and everybody gone for lunch. I laughed hysterically, took a deep breath and counted to ten. If you are not equipped with a boundless sense of humour, forget about doing anything more challenging than sunbathing in Morocco.

I went over to Yassin's café and told him about the quick deal.

"Good," he said curtly. He did not look up. He was busy chopping onions.

I wondered why he was upset. Was it because he had missed out on the commission? I had to give Mohamed three hundred dirham for his translating and negotiating. I wondered why my friend Yassin had been unable to help me and why I had had to rely on a stranger. There were politics, which I was unable to understand.

"Are you alright, Yassin?"

Yassin chopped and chopped.

"Of course."

"Will you sit and talk to me?"

"I have no time now."

I stayed by his side and rattled on in order to drown the silence of his non-existent input. Whatever had split us apart, I tried to persuade him to come back to me, to be my friend again, instead of this indifferent onion-chopping stranger. Our usual light-heartedness did not return, and realising, that I could do no more, I left.

I returned to the town hall, picked up all my neatly stamped, signed and dated documents and copies and presented them to the notary. Mr Abderrahim was going to register the land in my name, which would be done in ten days, *insha'allah*, so that I could then receive the papers, *insha'allah*, and also the papers for the land with my house on, *insha'allah*, which so far had not materialised. Unfortunately. One day I will be able to hold documents in my hand stating my ownership, *insha'allah*, but so far I had no proof at all. And I was already building a house on a piece of land, which was not exactly mine yet.

Chapter Fourteen

The morning was refreshingly cool. After breakfast, I walked up the stony track to Taliouine to check on the progress of my house. The air was clear and the light brown rolling hills, dotted with argan trees, stood out sharply against the blue sky. A rumbling sound in the distance announced a group of mountain people on their ancient mopeds on their way down to Taghazout.

I stopped to catch my breath and drank some water from my bottle. Three fishermen chugged past on backfiring bikes, churning up dust. Their heads were wrapped tightly in colourful fabrics, loose ends flapping cheerfully behind. The mopeds were laden with nets, buckets and all sorts of fishing gear.

"*Bonjour, Madame.*"

I waved after them and crossed the road to pick up the piste to Taliouine.

Yassin-the-builder came towards me, uncharacteristically light-footed, like a balloon bouncing down the hill.

He smiled. I looked behind me. There was nobody. Surely, he was not smiling at me, the woman, who insisted he built according to plans which reflected her wishes.

He braked to a halt in front of me. He was still smiling.

"*Madame – ifulki.*" He put his thumb up, hopefully referring to a positive progress concerning my house.

"*Ifulki*? You mean you built the upstairs room and are pleased with it?"I flashed a cautious smile at him.

The builder nodded. "*Ifulki*," he repeated and bounced off towards his pick-up van.

Hopefully we would continue on such an amiable basis.

Whistling, I entered my house and looked around. Things were indeed progressing according to plan. I climbed up the wooden ladder and froze. Here I was in my little upstairs room, but then again – I was not. Where I had planned a window, there was an opening for a door. And instead of the door I had envisaged there was a window. There was a wall cutting the room in two, which I had not intended. I grabbed my bottle of water tightly and stepped out onto the terrace. There was no hole for the rain pipe in the corner of the terrace.

Ifulki? Did he think it was beautiful how he had redesigned my upstairs? He had been so proud. I rested my elbows on the balustrade and stared into the valley. It did not improve my mood to find the main electricity cables had been put up. Thick, black and annoying they crisscrossed my view and made it look like a broken mirror. I emptied my water bottle slowly down onto the quiet village path.

And downstairs - was there really a water pipe under the freshly concreted floor? Maybe the builder had decided that I would not need any water. Maybe I was meant to get a donkey and go to the well every other day like many of the village women. Maybe he was right.

I threw the empty bottle against the unwanted wall and left.

Marching down to Taghazout I realised that I was not prepared to spend another evening adjusting my plans to the builder's spontaneities. I was going to face him. Tell him what I thought about him. *Ifulki*! I snorted.

I found the builder slouching in a self-satisfied manner against the counter of his DIY stall. He smiled. I did not.

"Yassin's café!" I commanded and turned.

To my surprise, he followed me.

"Yassin, help me," I stormed into the café. "He just doesn't do what he is supposed to do. He did everything wrong."

I made Yassin translate my several complaints which my friend delivered weakly, avoiding the builder's stare.

"The staircase. Don't forget to tell him about the staircase. It is in the wrong place," I urged my poor friend.

The happy bouncy builder from the mountains had vanished. The man opposite me, whose face was distorted with anger, took his pencil and violently stabbed my plans, probably defending his re-positioning of the staircase. He sounded all together alarmingly spiteful, got up and stormed out of the cafe.

Yassin had found an interesting crumb on the table to pick and did not look at me. I should stop dragging him into my disputes. Another unpleasant task like this and our friendship might not be able to take the strain.

"Sorry, Yassin," I sighed. "I should not do this to you."

He flicked the crumb off the table. I watched it land on the balding fur of one of the sick looking village cats which was sleeping in the shadows. Or had it died?

"I want to help, but is difficult," he said. "Too much for my head."

I knew this expression. It was one of his favourites. Many things were too much for Yassin's head. Everyone has some odd things about him, I thought and liked Yassin nevertheless. I had always been able to count on him in the past when it had been necessary.

There were strong forces in the male orientated society of Taghazout, which I could only guess. Men were spending every day of their lives here, on the scene from morning to late evening. Life and work was happening in the village. There was no possibility to escape physically. To ensure a more or less peaceful existence there must be lots of unwritten rules and a strict hierarchy which either had to be respected or risk was taken to become an outcast.

I was ashamed that I was making it difficult for Yassin.

I got up. "I'd better go now," I said.

"You don't want *tajine*?" Yassin asked.

"Thank you, Yassin, but I have a lot to do."

109

"Come back tomorrow. Or when you have time," he called after me.

A cold wind was blowing across the blue sunny morning sky and I had to dig out a thick jumper from the depths of my van.

The builder's team tried to repair the damage. The wall was taken down, while I tried to simplify my plan as much as I could. Abdullah, the henchman, spent hours hacking a hole through the corner of the terrace for the rain pipe.

A shadow fell over my drawings. I looked up and shielded my eyes.

"Yassin! What a surprise. You did not tell me yesterday that you were coming."

"I had time and wanted to look at your house," my friend answered, his baseball cap pulled almost over his eyes.

"Come on, let's have a look." I jumped up and we entered my house.

Yassin looked here and there, sniffing around like a little animal.

"Yassin, are you alright?" I laughed. "What are you looking for?"

"Nice house," he said, dashing forwards and backwards.

"What is wrong?" I grabbed his arm.

He had not smiled once.

"He did not pay my commission," Yassin mumbled, poking his finger through a porous breezeblock.

"Oh no, Yassin, I am sorry. What can I do?"

He shifted uncomfortably.

"Me, I go back to Taghazout. Much work." And with this he left the house.

"Yassin! Talk to me!" I shouted, watching him walk away. I did not want a wall of unspoken words building up between us.

He turned and called: "He sent me to tell you he wants more money."

I went straight down to Taghazout. I made my way through the usual mixture of heat, dust and bustle, and bumped into Yassin-the-builder. I was about to open my mouth, when he said, "Yassin café!"

I nodded and walked on. I did not want my friend Yassin to translate for me. I was looking for someone else. Taghazout is small place with the male population always around and it did not take long, until Hamid, the teacher from Taliouine crossed my path.

"Hamid!"

He stopped. *"Bonjour Madame, ca va?"*

Did this man never smile?

"Bonjour, merci, ca va bien, et vous?"

We continued with the customary exchange of polite enquiries until all subjects were exhausted and I was free to ask him, if he was prepared to act as a translator for me. He looked at me as if I had asked a rude thing of him, and it made me blush. He will say no, I thought, and I will be completely embarrassed. Meanwhile we were surrounded by onlookers, who were keen to watch the foreign women trying to pick up a young Moroccan man.

"Of course I will. I am honoured."

We wandered off towards Yassin's café. The onlookers cheered.

We sat down on the terrace. The café was empty. I watched the cars go by, aware of the awkward silence between Hamid and me. I felt he was judging me and did not approve of me. Just like Tobin. I was back eight years ago, when out of fear of not saying the right things and being ridiculed I switched into mute mode. Hamid did not talk either and I was relieved when the builder stomped up the steps.

He pulled a dishcloth from his jacket and mopped his moist forehead. He glanced at me, then at Hamid by my side and marched straight past to the counter, where magically my friend Yassin had materialised. They had a heated whispered discussion, and Yassin seemed to be shrinking in his skin and trying to disappear behind the counter at the same time. Finally the builder turned round and headed for the door. He was leaving.

111

I leaped up and stepped into his way, practically forcing him to sit down at the table, unless he was going to push me aside.

There was a long talk between the builder and Hamid in Arabic, which can be summarised in one sentence. Yassin the builder wanted the remaining twenty thousand dirham. I was relieved. This problem was easy to deal with.

"No," I said. "Only when the work is finished. As agreed." End of story, end of meeting.

Later Yassin said to me: "You could have at least given him five thousand dirham."

"Is that your commission, Yassin?" I retorted and left.

For the rest of the day I was brooding over my plans to adjust the layout to the builder's latest creativity. The staircase in the far corner was a difficult problem to overcome, as it did not leave enough headroom for the bathroom underneath. The builder had drawn chalk lines on the wall to indicate where he needed the shuttering for the staircase. I wiped them off and chalked my own staircase on the wall, so I would be able to move around in the bathroom without banging my head on the stairs. However, I was not too sure about it. As the next day was going to be a Sunday, there would be nobody working on the house and I could make a decision about it.

I drove down to the beach, but the plan still occupied my mind. When I went to bed, I had worked out a way where the staircase could be left as the builder had drawn it. In fact, he had placed them in a perfect position! After breakfast I would go upstairs and wipe the lines I had drawn out again. I had time. No one would be working on a Sunday.

DOWN TOWARDS THE SEA

Chapter Fifteen

I arrived early on Sunday morning only to find the building site bustling with activity. A dozen workers had been busy putting up the shuttering for the staircase – according to the lines I had drawn on the wall.

"*Madame, Madame!*" Proudly, everyone waved and pointed at the future staircase.

I screwed up my plan into a small ball and kicked it down the hill. From now on I was going to spend the nights up here to be the first one on the site and the last one to leave so as not to miss vital developments.

I found a level spot on the other side of Moulham's field, near the vast concrete expanse of the new cistern which was waiting for the first rain to catch water for the village people.

Apart from occasional visits to the site, there was nothing for me to do. Best part of my day was spent with feeding a herd of goats with banana skins and vegetable peels. The curious animals had surrounded my van, filling it with a hot goatee smell. The bleating was sad and pathetic.

I felt lonely. Here I was, on the edge of the village, locally and socially, with no one to talk to but sad smelly goats. Here I was, in my precious van which had once been the symbol of my freedom and had now become a prison. I had long realised that pain travels with you wherever you go. In the beginning, the excitement of travelling was great. There was no need to worry, to think. It was like a never-ending film, a story, with me being the heroine. I was in control. I could always move on. I never had to compromise. If I did not like places, people or weather, I moved on. When memories started to haunt me I moved on. Travelling was my drug. But there came the time when I had been everywhere. And the places I had not been to did not interest me much.

I stared at the red sun, which was descending rapidly.

And while I had set off to escape people I now found myself longing for their company. At times I had been so used to being without communication that asking for bread in a bakery made me blush. The sound of my own voice embarrassed me.

I watched people coming home from their day's occupation in Taghazout. Soon every family would sit around their low wooden table and share a tajine. There would be laughter, shrieks, arguments, love and hate, gloom and joy, singing and talking.

After sunset, the sky darkened rapidly. The village closed its door on me. The damp smell of sea reached my nostrils.

I had hardly moved all day.

Stiffly I got up. I needed something to cheer me up.

I rummaged through the cupboards for a cigarette, then stepped outside into the cool evening.

I could hear no sound other than the waves far below. Without electricity, there was only the light of the stars and the moon. They seemed twice as near and twice as bright as anywhere else I had been. Everything was bathed in a soft protective shine. It reminded me of the night light I used to leave burning during those dreadful episodes when Tobin withdrew from me for days, even weeks, refusing to talk to me.

The peacefulness and the diffused light comforted me, and I forgot about the cigarette.

The following day the outside plastering started. Scaffolding crawled up the walls, a messy construction of uneven pieces of wood. Men without helmets and safety shoes balanced precariously over the narrow planks, juggling with mortarboards and trowels and throwing great big slabs of cement against the wall. The mood was nevertheless cheerful.

"*Bonjour Madame*," I was greeted by a sea of swaying trowels.

"*Bonjour Messieurs*," I shouted back, hoping none of the men would fall off.

I loved the way the plaster undulated on top of the grey breezeblocks, hiding all straight lines.

Soon the builder would have fulfilled his part of the contract. It was time for me to organise workers and materials for the internal plastering, bricklaying and painting. Cherifa's anger over not employing her son Yassin shot through my head.

There was something my neighbour could do for me.

My newly acquired piece of land had to be levelled and concreted. I was eager to leave the exposed spot by the field and install my van on *le parking* next to the house.

I knocked on the bright blue door of Yassin's house.

"Yassin!" I heard water splashing in the yard.

The perfumed smell of *Teide* escaped through the holes in the wall. Yassin pulled the door open. Behind him, Mina was washing clothes in a faded blue plastic bowl. Jalal was sitting on the floor baking mud cakes.

"*La bes, Madame, bejer*," Yassin greeted.

Mina got up and wiped her hand on her makeshift apron.

"*Atei, Madame.* " Forever hospitable, she waved me to come in.

"*Shokran, Mina*, I have no time for tea, *oho, après*."

She giggled and crouched back in front of her bowl. The yard was decorated with tiny garments and colourful fabrics.

Jalal held up a handful of mud and smiled.

"Yassin – *tu veux travailler*?" I asked my neighbour.

His face lit up.

"*Merci, Madame.*" He stepped out of his yard and, without saying another word to Mina, pulled the door shut.

We walked over to my new piece of land, which was littered with ragged children of all sizes and shapes.

"*Sir!*" Yassin hissed.

Shrieking and laughing, they ran off, in unison like a flock of starlings, and settled on Cherifa's *farine*.

"Yassin, I need concrete – *cimar* – here, *ici* and *ici*, because this is going to be *le parking* for my *camion* and it has to be level – *comme ca*, and *ici* – a little wall – *murs* – only this height, made from *bric*." I stopped, rather embarrassed by my choice of words as if talking to an imbecile. Probably, I had spoken really slowly and even shouted, like some people do when they mistake language problems for hearing impairment.

"*Pas de problème, Madame.*" Yassin waved his hand dismissively.

I laughed. For my neighbour, problems were non-existent. I liked this about him. Hopefully, he would not make pregnant Mina lay down the concrete.

Yassin indicated me to wait and dashed into Nashiema's house. Seconds later he re-appeared with Mohamed in tow who was still half-asleep.

I did not mind if they shared the work. They reckoned that it was *beaucoup de travaux* and that it would at least take seven days to finish it.

"Five days," I said.

"*C'est bien, Madame,*" they agreed.

The two of them together would probably need only three days, but we agreed that for five hundred dirham each, my neighbours Yassin and Mohamed would level and concrete the strip of land and build a low wall around it.

It was probably too much money. I seemed to pay too much to everybody, but I couldn't justify to myself paying less. The wages were ridiculously low already and I did not want to exploit my neighbours. So I ended up overpaying them, and everybody knew and smirked at the daft foreign woman who could easily be taken advantage of. I did not mind. Not yet.

116

Meanwhile the third side of the house was being plastered, nice uneven handmade plaster, not the neat European style. It gave my square and plain looking house a tiny touch of artistic flair.

I walked up onto the second floor and watched the shuttering for the staircase to the top terrace going up – surprise, surprise - in the right place!

The world was brightening up again. The building work was proceeding. Yassin and Mohamed would build *le parking*.

This reminded me that Yassin and Mohamed needed building materials. I had to organize a lorry-load of gravel, cement and sand. And I had no idea what to do about it.

When I mentioned this to Yassin and Mohamed they showed me round various dwellings where leftovers of earlier building activities were piled up in the corners.

"Madame – *pas cher*," Mohamed tried to convince me.

I did not want to buy leftovers because I had no idea of cost. I did not know the price for a sack of gravel, or cement. Or for a brick. And anyway, I would be needing more in the future and I had to find out where and how to get hold of it.

"*Oho*, no." I shook my hand. "I want to buy a lorry load, a *camion. Tu compris?*"

Yassin and Mohamed laughed. "*Oui, oui.*"

"And where can I buy it? Taghazout?"

"Taghazout? *Oho. Oho* Taghazout." They shook their heads vehemently as if I had asked if there was a nudist beach in the village.

"So – where then? Tamraght?" It was not easy to extract information from my two neighbours.

Yassin straightened his shirt and brushed dust off his trousers.

"*Madame*," he said. "Aourir."

He walked past me towards my van.

"*Azih, azih, Madame.*"

I fumbled for my key and ran after him.

The market square in Aourir was packed with old-fashioned yellow lorries. Heavy pre-war Margius Deutz trucks, discarded by the rich West and handed down to the third world, were waiting here for orders.

Yassin and I split up, because he had met some friends or family members and was exchanging enquires about the health of various relatives.

It was going to be a difficult task to find a lorry driver who would quote a genuine price to a tourist. I strolled along the line of lorries and men. It was like trying to find the best apple in an orchard. I stared at the men, and they stared at me, neither friendly nor hostile, but curious and intense. Conversations ceased. My feet grew heavier and heavier. I was embarrassed. Maybe I could just walk on towards the beach, pretending that's where I had intended to go in the first place.

"*Bonjour, Madame.*" A middle-aged man in a dark blue boiler suit stepped forwards. His rolled up sleeves bared suntanned muscular arms. *One more Tequila* was written on the cap, he was wearing back to front on his head. "You need help?"

"Yes." Gratefully I drifted towards him. "I am building a house and I need materials."

"Larbi my name." Larbi nearly shook my arm out of its socket.

Most of the drivers gathered around us when Larbi gave me a lecture on how to order building materials. It appeared to be even less straight forward than I had anticipated. There was a complicated system as to what was going to be delivered and how much money it cost. An insider language was being used which I found very difficult to grasp.

There was *fer* (steel), *sable* (sand), *cimar* (cement) and *gravel* (gravel). *Fer* and *sable* might be *un bon* (free) when buying *cimar* and *gravel*. On the other hand, you might be asked to pay an astronomic sum for all four and then find that steel was not included after all.

"So, how much does it cost then?"

He laughed.

"Forty thousand."

I gasped. My whole house had not been that expensive.

As experienced with Moulham, there was a wide spread difficulty in communicating numbers, not only due to illiteracy but also to the fact that the Moroccan people use different currencies.

In the more recent parts of the towns, especially the ones frequented by tourists, a price is clearly quoted in dirham and centimes. A price tag saying 5,60 is indeed what it seems: five dirham and sixty centimes.

Elsewhere in town - the old medina, for example - where communication is in French, prices will be quoted in *franc*. It is by no means the same as the *franc* in France: one *franc* in Morocco equals one centime.

Some of the old people use the *rial*, a currency which was replaced in 1921. One *rial* equals ten dirham.

Additionally, Berber money and mountain money is used, but due to its incomprehensibility I don't even want to try and work out an explanation.

As I never proceeded past writing "*table of conversion*" on a blank sheet of paper, I had to rely on the more graphic explanations of the sellers.

Larbi pulled out a wad of money and counted out the amount he was expecting me to pay. Did this mean that all the lorry drivers walked around with about one thousand two hundred dirham in their pockets?

My neighbour Yassin appeared and pushed a weasel-like man in front of me, whose eyes darted about like pin balls.

"Lahcen – *demain, insha'allah – bon prix*," Yassin introduced his friend.

What a shame Yassin interfered when I was just about to close a deal! However, I had asked him to help because I thought I could not do it on my own.

Larbi shrugged his shoulders and walked back to his lorry.

"*Shokran*," I shouted after him. "*A la prochaine*."

"*Insha'allah, Madame*."

Satisfied, I drove back to Taliouine. It had been easy and straightforward. I was looking forward to the next morning.

At seven o'clock the next morning, I was lurking around outside my building site to witness the arrival of my first delivery of buildings material. I cleared gravel and weed from *le parking* in preparation. I swept in front of my house. I swept Yasmina's path.

It was eight o'clock and there was no sign of a lorry making its way up to Taliouine. To be honest, I had half expected this to happen because nothing in Morocco was ever easy and straightforward.

Yassin and Mohamed appeared several hours later, after a good lie-in.

"No *camion*," I greeted them.

They shook their heads and tutted empathetically, walked off and returned carrying the leftovers in their arms.

"*Madame*?" Mohamed asked, looking innocent.

"Go on; use the old rubbish," I waved my hand." That's what you wanted to do all the way long."

I wondered what they were going to charge me. I had lost control, and I was disappointed about myself. How could I let it slip out of my hands so easily? Had Yassin organised the lorry not to come in order to get rid of the villagers' leftovers? However clever I was trying to be, someone was always a step ahead of me.

For a while, I watched Mohamed and Yassin. Silently, with furrowed foreheads, they cleared *le parking*, levelled it and prepared it for the laying of concrete. A throng of village children surrounded them, screaming, pushing each other; noses still oozing green slime. Mohamed took Samir and wiped his nose with his fingers, which he then cleaned on one of the bricks. The boys haggled over a toy, a small tyre, then drove it along the path with a stick. None of the children had factory made toys.

Two days later, there was a knock on the door of my van. My neighbours Yassin and Mohamed stood outside, hands in pockets.

"Any problems?" There had not been any for two days, and I had started to feel uncomfortable, thinking the more time passed with everything running smoothly the bigger the price I would have to pay.

"No problem, *Madame*," Mohamed shook his head with emphasis, "*le parking – fini*." He clapped his hands, signalling the end of the work.

"You are joking. You only started two days ago."

Hassan smiled.

We walked across the field to the parking, which was drying in the sun - a slap of wet cement, with a line of village children along the side where I had expected to see a low brick wall. Big brown eyes were staring at me expectantly.

I guessed that if Mohamed and Yassin had taken five days I would have ended up with a level piece of concrete with a neat row of bricks around to stop "*le parking*" being washed down to Taghazout by the next rain. But with its undulating surface and the fringed edges it looked as if it had already struggled to keep its position in several flush floods.

Mohamed and Yassin beamed at me.

"*Ifulki*." I sighed.

The village children clapped and cheered.

Mohamed and Yassin grinned.

"Now please build a brick wall."

"*Eyeh, Madame*."

The next day the brick wall was finished, leaning drunkenly towards the sea.

Mohamed and Yassin were standing next to me awaiting more praise.

"Well, at least it has character," I murmured.

To talk business, I was invited into Mohamed's house. Nashiema prepared tea, while the dark heads of my two builders were hovering over a shabby piece of paper on which they were calculating the value of the building materials.

We had the obligatory three glasses of tea, served with warm bread and *Amlou*, a sweet paste made from peanuts and argan oil.

After that, Mohamed cleared his throat and named the price.

I splattered the rest of my tea back into the glass and got up.

"*Attende.*" I snapped the piece of paper and the pencil and set off to the parking.

They had used forty bricks, two bags of cement and two sacks of sand which even by setting a generous price added up to only a fraction of Mohamed's calculation.

I returned to the house and presented my figures.

Yassin and Mohamed laughed.

"*Wacha, Madame, ca va,*" Yassin accepted in his laid-back sing sang voice.

It seemed to be a game which everybody played here: let's see how much we can get out of her and if it does not work today, then maybe tomorrow, *insha'allah*!

Fuming, I swore to myself that I would never work with Yassin and Mohamed again. Even if I was going to be poisoned by Cherifa for it!

Chapter Sixteen

Sitting in the early morning sun near the *farine*, I listened to Yasmina's trademark chicken-like clucking and the hissing sound of her broom crisscrossing the narrow pathway. Clouds of dust were stirred up into the air, only to settle down again a little later. There was a rumour that Cherifa wanted to sell the path, but so far, nobody had approached me. How would Yasmina get into her house, anyway, without the path leading up to her front door? There was not much she could do, as the land belonged to her mother, and when Cherifa scented dirham, nothing could stop her.

My house was progressing nicely. In preparation for the concrete laying, the uneven floor had to be levelled by filling the gaps with rocks. As the hillsides were strewn with stones of all shapes and sizes, the builder's workforce swarmed out with buckets and wheelbarrows and collected what they needed. Hopefully the cistern would not collapse under the weight of a small mountain.

The staircase to my roof terrace had been finished. I walked up the steps and found myself above the village. Excitedly, I turned round like a spinning top. There was nothing blocking my view across the ocean and the beach, the hills and the neighbouring villages. I leant over the wall and looked down into the village. With a start, I realised, that in a voyeur's fashion I could look into my neighbour's houses. I saw Yasmina darting from her kitchen into the courtyard and back. Nadah and Cherifa were crushing argan nuts in their yard. I was mortified. I had no intention of spying on my neighbours. What if one of them suddenly looked up and caught me staring at them? I pulled my head back. Never ever would I look down over the wall again.

Contrary to most days, when the site teemed with masons, only one man was working on the outside of the house. Naturally, his name was Yassin. Yassin-the-bricklayer, for easier identification. Yassin-the-bricklayer was plastering the rest of the house speedily, his forehead creased into a frown of determination. He did not stop for lunch, not even for a drink. He moved precariously across a fragile-looking construction made from ladders and planks of wood.

"Yassin!" I called.

Before he could faint and crash five metres down to the ground I'd better offer him some nourishment. I pointed at a loaf of bread, jam, oranges and a bottle of water which I had placed on the floor for him. He smiled and climbed down. He sank to the floor in the shade of the house, his back slumping against the wall. With big noisy gulps, he almost finished the bottle of water, greedily sucked the juice from the oranges and ate all the bread. I watched him. He was much younger than I had thought, maybe eighteen or twenty years old.

"It is dangerous to work hard and not to eat and drink." I explained my words by using hands and feet, as I had got used to doing. My Berber was not coming on as nicely as I had wished. I had not progressed further than the greetings and some useful imperatives.

Yassin understood me, and I understood him. Yassin-the-builder had told him to finish the rendering of the house. If not, he Yassin-the-bricklayer would lose his job.

Yassin-the-bricklayer worked from 7 o'clock until sunset with only one short break which I had imposed on him. He finished the plastering and was exhausted. The builder did not even turn up to fetch him. Yassin had to walk all the way down to Taghazout. I paid him some extra money for the work he had done. I liked him. He seemed perfect for the second phase of the building process, when Yassin-the-builder's job would be finished and I had to take over myself. With someone like Yassin-the-bricklayer in my team I would feel much better.

The village people had started to supply me with freshly baked bread which I thought to be very kind and hospitable. Especially, as I could no longer indulge in the fresh bread from Taghazout's bakery, spending my nights in the mountain village. And there was no point in bulk buying it during my trips down to the fishing village, because after two days the bread was as hard and dry as cardboard. I was also determined to take it as a sign that people were warming towards me.

Moulham inspected *le parking* and told me, that the foundations of the adjoining house needed to be stabilised.

"*Moi, je fait. Trois cent dirham,*" he offered himself for the job.

Three hundred dirham seemed a bargain, considering that it quite possibly prevented my unknown neighbour's house from collapsing. According to Moulham. I agreed. Moulham grinned and walked off.

Once he started, Moulham worked hard. Not only did he stabilise the foundations of the house, but he also tried to improve Mohamed and Yassin's work. He shook his head and muttered while tackling *le parking*, probably calling it the Berber equivalent of a botch job.

"*Shokran*, Moulham," I said and sat down on the low wall.

"*De rien, Madame,*" Moulham replied, mopping his forehead with a cloth.

I wondered how old he was. His childlike build with the weather-beaten face, wrinkly and brown as an old apple, made it hard to guess. He was probably somewhere between sixty and ninety. He could be very friendly and kind, bringing fish, yoghurts or bread up from Taghazout. But I had seen him turn ice cold and fearsome within seconds, still with a smile on his lips. I did not want to have him as an enemy. Despite his elfin appearance, he was the boss of the village and people were in awe of him.

"Madame – Agadir?" he asked

"*Oui, peut-être.*" I answered cautiously.

"*Cent dirham – achetez litro.*"

He wanted me to buy wine for one hundred dirham, four litre-bottles of table wine. I declined.

"*Non, Monsieur, je suis désolée.*" I got up and walked away.

Islam was not in favour of alcohol, demanding abstinence from its people. I did not want to be involved, if someone decided to go against the word of the Koran.

Chapter Seventeen

In no time, our medieval village arrived in the 21st century.

Next to Cherifa's house a grey concrete mast had shot out of the ground, thin and wiry arms stretching out at the top ready to embrace the electricity cable. No doubt, they were going to follow soon. The mast was anchored in the dusty path with a lump of concrete which looked as if the earth had spat out something indigestible.

My neighbours had taken to grouping around it like children around a Christmas tree – awestruck, with wide eyes. Who could blame them? The long forgotten mountain villages were finally connected to the real world.

It was another beautiful morning, and I was lingering outside my house, doing nothing else but soaking up the warmth and brightness like a sponge. I was becoming more and more accustomed to the lifestyle in the sun. Squinting, I noticed a man dressed in European style trousers and shirt, running his hand up and down the rough surface of the concrete mast.

I tore myself away from my sun bathing and approached him. I was curious, why a man with the air of a town dweller was fascinated by this latest addition to our village. Maybe I had discovered the Moroccan equivalent to a train spotter.

"*Bonjour, Monsieur*," I called.

He turned abruptly.

"*Bonjour, Madame*."

He stretched his mast-patting hand out. I shook it.

"I came to see you, *Madame*." Glancing back at the mast like a proud father he continued: "Isn't it beautiful?"

"Perhaps...maybe.... I would not call it beautiful."

"You would not?" He looked at me.

I had said the wrong thing. "Beautiful is probably not the right word. Functional, yes, they are functional. And progressive."

We nodded in unison. He looked at me approvingly.

It was no good. I had to voice my disappointment.

"No, I don't like it, personally. Look what they do to the view." I beckoned him over to the *farine*. "Look at the wires everywhere. Do you call this beautiful?"

I did not wait for an answer.

"And listen – listen, what can you hear?"

Although he looked at me as if I had gone mad, he listened.

"I can hear, donkeys, children, someone is singing...and waves, I can even hear the waves." He was astonished.

"That's right. But it will not stay like this. Soon we will hear radios and television blaring out loudly."

The man shifted.

"And in the night, we won't see the moon and the stars anymore, because unattractive light bulbs will be lighting up the village in the future. It just doesn't fit. Do you think I should like it?"

"But *Madame*!" He threw up his hands in despair. "Life will be so much better now for the village people."

I sighed. It was the same everywhere, the craving for mod cons. Emptiness. Loss of identity. The resulting loneliness. This man and I will not be able to agree. Maybe one day I will be able to speak to the responsible people and then...

"...*Madame*."

"Sorry, I did not hear. What did you say?" I woke up from my musings.

"I said my name is Najib. I am the electrical engineer, responsible for this project. I will give you my telephone number, in case you decide to let your house be wired up and connected to the mains. We can do it for you."

I could imagine that all my neighbours had the desire to connect to TV, radio and light, but could they afford it?

"Have you connected anybody yet?" I asked hoping it would be as far away from my house as possible.

"No, *Madame*, in this village nobody is going to have the wiring done at the moment. It is very expensive."

"I don't want to be connected either," I said.

"*Madame*, your house should at least be wired. Then you can connect to the mains whenever you want. The house will also be worth more, if you want to sell it."

"I haven't even finished building it, how can you think I would want to sell it? Anyway, not having any electricity or gas or running water is just what I like about this village."

"*Madame*, please, this is the 21st century. You cannot pretend it has not arrived here in Morocco. I advise you to get your house wired up now, before you decorate inside. I will make you a good price."

Najib explained that channels had to be cut into the breezeblock walls and wires had to be cemented in. Switches and plugs had to be fixed and connected to the wires. Tons of fuses would be needed and kilometres of cable, pipes and wires.

There was truth in what Najib said. I could still live with solar panels and candle light, but in the future, I would have the choice. Who knows, maybe my need for a natural life was temporary. I have known myself for long enough to assume that this phase would not last forever.

"And of course you need the cut-out-unit. Without it, we are not allowed to connect you to the main cable."

Cut-out-unit? What was it going to cut out? Chains of paper dolls? Newspaper articles?

As it turned out it was nothing like as entertaining. The unit simply would cut the supply of electricity if there was a fault so my house would not blow up. It was a legal requirement and probably equally expensive as important.

The price Najib quoted for the wiring was high by Moroccan standard. In England, no electrician would even change a light bulb for that kind of money.

"Here is my telephone number. Phone me, if you want to go ahead," he said. He tore a corner off a document he was carrying and scribbled an assortment of numbers on the back of it.

I was going to think about it.

Chapter Eighteen

Over the next few of days, the building work came slowly to an end.

Abdullah the hunch man had been busying himself with the last remaining job: digging a channel for the pipe, which was going to connect the toilet with the soak-away. It worried me slightly that I could not see a pipe for this purpose lying around anywhere. The builder might have it tucked away in his car.

"Yassin!"

Yassin-the-builder crawled from a dark corner of my house, wiping his sleepy eyes. He had made it his habit to come upstairs for a two-hour nap in the cool shadow of the site.

"*Ifulki.*" I put my thumps up.

The builder grunted.

I went for a walk through the village.

The channel was cemented shut before I had a chance to convince myself that there was actually a pipe inside.

I stared at the fresh cement on the floor and then at the builder. He stared back.

Did he, or did he not? He would not dare, would he?

We stared at each other until he broke into a grin. He spat on the floor and walked off, probably amused by the idea of me flushing the contents of my toilet into the soak-away via an empty channel.

Yassin-the-bricklayer had finished building the wall to the bedroom, leaving a gaping window-sized hole near the ceiling.

"Yassin, *ce n'est pas fini*," I said.

Yassin-the-bricklayer shook his head, indicating that there were no more breezeblocks left. I stomped off and found the builder in his car, listening to a squeaking tape of Arabic pop music.

"You need to get more bricks. *Azih*." I shouted.

The builder scrambled out of his car and followed me.

I pointed at the unwanted window in my bedroom wall.

"*Ah – oui, c'est bon pour ventilation*." The builder was enthusiastic. He fanned himself with both hands, in case I had not understood and was probably going to charge extra for this fresh air hole.

It did not improve my mood to find him speaking French after all.

"*Oho*, Yassin." I waggled my finger Berber style. "I don't want a hole. Please bring more bricks."

"*Eyeh*, Madame," the builder said. He returned to his car and turned the music up.

He was not going to deliver more bricks. All I could do was to adopt his idea of ventilation. And did not all rooms in Berber houses have these types of ventilation windows, even though they were considerably smaller?

It was Sunday morning, ten o'clock, when Yassin-the-builder blocked my path.

"*L' argent – midi*." He stabbed at his watch.

"The banks are closed on Sundays," I told him. "*Fermer*."

"*Fermer, fermer*," he muttered, then shouted as if I was deaf: "*MIDI*!"

"The banks are closed today. *FERMER*!" I shouted back, slowly and loudly, as if he was the village idiot.

And so we continued until he finally decided to understand.

"*Demain – midi. Ghedda*."

With a last fierce glance and an eruption of threatening language, he squeezed into his pick-up and disappeared down the track leaving me coughing from dust and car fumes.

When the air cleared again, Moulham appeared.

"No good man." He shook his head.

"No good manners, to say the least."

Moulham who was fond of gossiping had his mind already set on the latest village rumour.

"Nashiema – *Gendarmerie* Taghazout." His eyes glinted, displaying as usual inappropriate joy at the misfortune of Cherifa's family. "Mohamed – *troubles avec les touristes!*" Moulham grinned.

"*Arrêtez.*" I said. "It is not very nice to be euphoric when your neighbours are in trouble. You are the boss here, you should help." I walked towards my house, leaving Moulham with his grin frozen to his face.

It was a typical spring morning in Agadir, with the sun shining warmly from a perfectly blue sky. The tourists were heading for the sandy beach. Young girls in immaculate white frocks were on their way to school, chatting excitedly. The people of Agadir were going about their daily work, from stallholders in the souk to estate agents in the state-of-the-art glass buildings. Almost like in any other major town in any other country.

Agadir, my new home, I thought whilst walking along the main boulevard to the bank. I strode purposefully. I was not a tourist. I was a member of the community, and I, too, was going about my daily work. My head held up self-confidently I tried to blend in.

"*Madame*, buy handbag, ring, necklace." A young Moroccan shot out of a small shop.

"*La, shokran,*" I answered in my best Arabic, bowing slightly and touching my heart briefly with my right hand, as I had observed my friend Yassin do.

"*Madame* speaks our language," the young man said, equally touching his heart and bowing.

Still bathing in this exchange of respect between a local man and the foreign-woman-who-moved-here, I slid my card into the dispenser of BMCI bank only to find that it was rejected.

I imagined arriving in Taghazout without a dirham in my pocket and having to tell the builder that I was not able to pay for his work after all, as he had feared all the time. I did not think I would survive his rage.

I phoned my bank. The coin phones only accepted thirty dirham at a time. After that, the connection broke off. I had to insert twenty more dirham and redial the number. As usual, it took three calls to get past reception and a fourth one to quickly shout the number of the booth into the receiver so the clerk could phone me back.

When she did, I heard that I had sufficient funds in my account.

I entered a different bank and after a complicated co-operation of credit and debit card I finally held twenty thousand dirham in my hand.

"Monday no good – always problem with computer," explained the man behind the counter helpfully. He had been very patient. Most likely, he had saved my life or at least my reputation.

At twelve o'clock I arrived at Yassin's café.

"Hello, Yassin."

"Hello, Kate."

Yassin was making paper serviettes.

"Everything alright?" I asked after a while. "Good business?"

Yassin shrugged his shoulders. "As usual." Tearing up paper into rectangles seemed to demand all his attention.

I was worried about the state of our friendship. We had lost our ease, our trust. I felt myself running up against a wall Yassin had erected. I wanted it to be as untroubled as it used to be, but I did not know what to do.

We were sitting in uncomfortable silence, waiting for the builder. I mentally made a list of "builder has done…, builder has not done…"

One hour later, Yassin-the-builder arrived, ogling me for signs of money.

My friend brought a tray of tea, and the three of us sat down together.

"I am happy with the house. Thank you for what you have done, Yassin. You did not plaster the inside though, and you did not install any doors and windows," I said.

My friend Yassin translated my complaint to the builder, who, short-tempered as usual, yelled at me in defence.

"He says it was not part of the contract," Yassin said.

The builder shook his head. His feisty fist landed on the table with a bang. The tea glasses jumped.

"Oh yes, it was. You must remember it. You saw the contract we drew up with Ahmed, Yassin. Tell him about it."

Yassin had already turned his attention to the road traffic in front of his cafe. "It is long ago, I don't really remember exactly every word."

"Not every word, Yassin, but every point. There were only nine points, and it was merely three weeks ago."

The conversation did not pick up again, and I could tell that I was expected to hand over the money at this point and consider the business as closed. I gave in. I did not want to haggle about minor matters. There was a shell of a house up on the hill, and it was mine. It had materialised within a few weeks, and although not exactly what I had aimed for, it was probably all I could achieve with this builder, and in this country.

Yassin-the-builder was obviously relieved, when I pulled out a bulging brown envelope. With unusual agility he leant forwards, snatched it out of my hands and stuffed it into the pocket of his tent-like *djellaba*. Before he left, he flashed his teeth at me in an attempt to smile.

My friend Yassin tried to catch my eye, but I was busy counting the cars going past the cafe.

Chapter Nineteen

Now that Yassin-the-builder had finished and withdrawn his army of workers, my house was sitting quietly on the hilltop - an austere shell with a ghostly air about it. I walked through the site, balancing on wooden planks over a patchwork of wet concrete. It smelled of damp cellars. It was my house, my new home, yet it felt hostile and discomfortingly unfamiliar. I had expected to have some kind of positive feeling towards it, like excitement or pride, but all I could think of was the huge amount of work that still needed to be done and that the responsibility was now mine. My feet stirred up a cockroach, which rushed up the wall like a silent black shadow. I shuddered and climbed up onto the roof terrace into the warmth of the sun.

I could not stop feeling cold. I tried to clear my throat, to dislodge a lump of uneasiness. Panic welled up, and I wondered if it was only the workload which upset me.

I was still an outsider. I realised that I was not going to be part of a circle of friends or a community simply by stopping travelling and building a house. I needed to work on the new relationships. However, had I chosen the right place? Would I be able to integrate myself into this village? And more importantly, would the people of Taliouine let me?

The same doubts were haunting me again and again. I could not relax and wait, have confidence in my decisions. Fear of failing had become my second nature in my life with Tobin, and it was difficult to change. If I succeeded here, would it not prove to me that I was strong?

I was tempted to pack my few belongings, throw them into my van and set off, as I would have done in the past, and forget about it all.

Where would I go, though, back to Europe, England, Germany, back to a job, a flat and the boredom of civilised life? It was not possible. I had come too far. I could not wipe out several years of travelling and freedom. They had changed me. I did not fit any more. I never fitted well anyway, but now it seemed impossible to even attempt it. I felt lost.

I recalled my knowledge of house building, but it did not go far beyond cardboard models and Lego.

The fact that I had not been able to win Yassin-the-bricklayer for my project had been a throwback.

"Tu..." – I had pointed at him – *"...travailles ici? Après?"*

I had been sure he would not decline. I would pay him well. I would treat him with respect, which is more than he would ever get from the overweight builder. He could have been the project manager. I would have left it all to him, because I felt I could trust him.

But he had declined. Regretfully, but still.

"Après la maison – pas de travailler." He had stumbled through his French vocabulary.

I understood his concern. Yassin-the-builder could offer him longer-term employment, and if he left him now to work for me, what would happen in a few weeks, when the house was finished? Yassin-the-bricklayer would be without a job. He would not be able to support his family any longer, who lived in a village near Taroudannt. It was not easy to find work. And although Yassin-the-builder was a slave driver, at least he paid.

Leaning my elbows on the terrace wall, I watched black dots bobbing on the waves far below. The fishermen were on their way to extract a meagre living from the vast ocean. Was this not what one was meant to do? Extract a living from the vastness of life? I was so much more privileged than the fishermen, than my neighbours in the village. Yet, here I was, moaning and feeling depressed at the number of choices given to me. I stretched and slapped the wall with my palms. I had no reason to complain. And somewhere in this vastness, there must be a trustworthy builder with a splatter of French, surely.

Impatient fists banged on the metal door accompanied by a twitter of cheerful voices. I looked over the terrace wall and saw a group of women, led by Cherifa. I rushed down the steps, hoping it was an amicable visit, and pulled the front door open.

"*Bonjour, Madame,*" the ladies chorused.

Cherifa stepped forwards.

"*Madame – shuf?*" She pointed at her eyes, then into the grey internal of the house.

"*Shuf?* Yes...of course. Have a look. *Eyeh, eyeh.* Come in. *Entrez.* " Excitedly, I waved them to come in.

The women filed in through the door, patting my hands, my arms, saying *la bes* and *bejer.* They took in every detail, asking questions, while I was trying to explain about kitchen, living area, bedroom and bathroom. The idea of a toilet made them shriek and giggle, then nod approvingly.

Finally, we had reached the top terrace. The women spread out like a colourful flock of birds and looked around, taking in the views.

"*Ifulki,*" one of them said.

The rest of the women nodded and put up their thumbs, smiling.

Cherifa leant over the terrace wall.

Smacha fulki rasa.

The women rushed to Cherifa's side. She was pointing down at her own house. Nadah was sitting in the yard, washing clothes in a plastic bowl.

The women's enthusiasm diminished. I was embarrassed. I had no intention of looking over the wall and intrude into their lives.

"*Mesdames*," I said. I pointed at my eyes and then down at the houses. "*Oho shuf!*" I waggled my finger.

The good mood returned, and I felt my back being patted affectionately.

The group made their way back downstairs and left.

After the short burst of colours and sounds, my house appeared more grey and silent than ever.

Armed with pencil and pad I walked through the house, noting down what had to be done. The whole of the inside had to be plastered and whitewashed. Shelves had to be built, and doors and windows to be ordered and fitted. Pipes had to be put in place everywhere. I yet had to work out a system, in which solar panels, pumps, toilet flushing and shower were connecting up to a satisfying cycle. It started to look a tad too ambitious for me, and I wondered if it was not easier to join my neighbours in the field instead.

I fled my house, which was now haunting me with its grey emptiness and its silent demand to do something about it.

Taghazout was as busy as usual. A throng of men with white *djellaba*s and white crocheted caps were on their way to Friday prayer in the mosque. I felt a tap on my shoulder and turned round.

"*Bonjour, Madame.*" A familiar face grinned at me.

"*Bonjour, Monsieur.*" Who was he? I had seen him before.

"Yassin my name. You talked to my brother. You look for builder."

It was Yassin-the-builder-who-was-in-Tiznit-and-would-be-back-in-a-few-days-*insha'allah*.

"*Bonjour*, Yassin-Tiznit," I cried and whisked him up to Taliouine before he could say he was busy, on his way to the mosque or back to Tiznit. I pulled him out of my van, shoved him into the house and made him look around.

"…and the walls have to be plastered, and here in the kitchen I need some shelves…"

Yassin-Tiznit took it all in, smiled and nodded.

"*Très jolie, Madame.*"

He liked my house. Hurray! He would work for me.

"Where can I invite you to, Yassin-Tiznit? Let's talk business," I said, eager to dine and wine him before his enthusiasm cooled down.

We could work out the details while we were in the café. I was determined to cling onto him until he promised to look after my house.

"Banana Village, *Chez Brahim*," Yassin-Tiznit said, rubbing his hands.

"You look like your brother," I said later, negotiating the potholes with my van.

"*Kif kif,*" he answered, knocking his index fingers against each other.

The same. Twins, I gathered.

Chez Brahim was a small insignificant roadside café in a row of others, not more than the usual garage-sized bar with a tiny counter. There were three tables inside and two outside, all covered with brightly coloured plastic cloths. The walls in the small room were tiled. They sported a typical Moroccan design with diamonds and flowers in green, blue and yellow.

We greeted Brahim, the owner, a small man with a bald patch on the top of his head. I was hungry and sank onto one of the chairs on the terrace, while Brahim and Yassin-Tiznit exchanged the customary greetings. The terrace bordered onto the main road, and I felt as if I was sitting on a traffic island. Water lorries and buses thundered past in a cloud of diesel fumes. The wind pulled my hair and covered the terrace in dust. The *clack clack* of a donkey drawing a carriage permeated my ear, followed by the penetrating sound of the defective exhaust of a small motorbike.

A madman huddled past, his hair matted and his skin the colour and texture of a turtle's. He was wearing nothing but a kind of loincloth, with his thin penis exposed. A cluster of ragged children followed him, shrieking and pointing their fingers at him.

"*Madame, azih.*"

141

I looked up to see Yassin-Tiznit, half way out of the café, beckoning me to follow him. We have not had tea and he was leaving already. I did not know where he was going, but got up.

"*Atei, s'il vous plait*," I ordered from Brahim on my way out, hoping with this to set a good omen for a timely return.

I caught up with Yassin-Tiznit at the butcher's stall. The customary sheep head on the counter with its blood-smeared stump of a neck never failed to churn my stomach. With empty eyes, it stared at its own hooves next to it, which sported clotted lumps of blood where they had been axed off the legs.

Yassin-Tiznit bought a slap of mincemeat. With the small parcel wrapped in yellowing newspaper, we walked back to Brahim's, zigzagging our way through road traffic and people, and jumping over unhealthy-looking oily puddles of unknown origin. Buckets of foul-smelling organic waste were waiting for collection and disposal in the dried out riverbed. They were buzzing with flies and crawling with beetles.

The madman squatted next to one of the buckets, helping himself to the rotting remains of fish guts and vegetable peels, scooping it out with his hands and stuffing it into his mouth like an animal. He sat hunched protectively, but his eyes were darting ceaselessly around. The cluster of children was nowhere to be seen. I marvelled at his skin, which was like a layer of leather. Living outside made him more an animal than a human. His eyes met mine, but moved on.

Back in the café, Brahim took our parcel and shaped the meat into flat round loaves, covered them in coriander and spices and flung them onto a barbeque the size of a pool table. It was called *kefta* and tasted of the freshest meat, the most succulent herbs and the most pungent spices I had ever come across. My eyes shut, when the sensations hit my taste buds.

Yassin-Tiznit made for unknown reasons a secret of his price. He enjoyed his *kefta* and mint tea, had an animated conversation with Brahim, but never mentioned my building site. We left the café and I agreed to meet him the next day on the beach outside Hassan's supermarket, where he was going to reveal his estimate. It suited me well, because at roughly the same time at the same place I would meet yet another Yassin-the-builder who was interested in the job.

The next day I waited for two hours on the beach at the agreed place. Finally, one of the Yassins came, telling me excitedly that he had met an old friend, which had kept him from seeing me in time. He needed half an hour more to catch up with all the old stories. I congratulated him on such great fortune and told him not to bother to come back after his catching up, which he took lightly.

Half an hour later Yassin-Tiznit arrived, but could not stay because he had a sick child at home. He could not take on the job either.

In a sudden bout of desperation, I drove to Agadir and bought a hand pump to be able to extract water from the cistern, while I was not connected to electricity. Electricity! It reminded me to phone Najib. He had been right. My house should at least have all the wires in place before the plastering started. I dialled the number he had written onto a scrap of paper.

"*Oui*?"

"Najib?"

"Najib?"

"Oui, Najib. *Je voudrais parler avec Najib, s'il vous plait!*"
I was starting to sweat.

"No Najib."

No Najib under this number. I must have dialled it wrongly.
"*Je suis désolée, Madame,*" I stammered and hung up.
I dialled again.

"*Oui!*"

"Najib? *Il est...*"

The woman hung up on me.

I crumpled up the piece of paper and kicked it down the path.

I had no idea how to contact Najib. I did not know where he lived, and nobody else seemed to know him.

Before finding a builder, I now had to find an electrician.

A hysteric giggle escaped.

I slowly counted to ten, and the panic subsided. My glance fell on the beautiful fire-engine red hand pump I had acquired. It was an old fashioned iron construction and weighed as much as a small motorbike. Once the cistern was cleaned out and filled with fresh water, it would be put to use.

No more lowering of dirty buckets by even dirtier ropes into the water. The cistern was going to be locked up.

I was proud of having achieved some kind of progress.

A couple of days later, my friend Yassin and I sat in the café together, trying to thaw out the ice between us.

He tried to help me calculating wages and borrowed my biro. "Hundred and thirty dirham a day..." - he wrote something into the palm of his hand and brooded over it for a long time - "...makes one thousand and three hundred dirham in ten days." He proudly showed me his palm in which he had written: 130 x 10 = 1300.

"I made appointment with electrician," Yassin suddenly said.

"You did?" I asked incredulously. "With Najib? How did you manage, Yassin? That is really great."

My friend Yassin had organised a meeting with Najib the electrician! It surprised me as to how Yassin had been able to. Maybe Najib had walked past, or even had come to Yassin's café. Morocco is a small place.

Yassin smiled. "You come to café tomorrow ten o'clock."

Chapter Twenty

At the appointed time, I was sitting at one of the tables with my friend.

"You are happy? Everything is going well?" Yassin enquired.

I heard concern in his voice and was touched. Maybe I had only imagined cracks in our friendship. Thinking he was disloyal was probably due to me being too sensitive. It was not the first time in my life it had caused misunderstandings. Maybe the builder had been bullying him.

"Yes, things are going alright." I scanned the terrace, which was empty except for a haggard looking man, who was exhaling the smoke from his cigarette like an angry bull.

While we were waiting for Najib, we chatted away like in old times.

"When your house is finished, you must give a party," Yassin said. "Everyone from the mountains will come."

It sounded a lot considering that there were four villages already on the surrounding hilltops. Mountains – what did it include: Marrakesh? Midelt?

"And you must give wine." He leant forwards, his blue eyes glinting. "You give only tea – and everybody will sleep."

The thin man lit another cigarette with small hectic movements.

Yassin explained further: "Men need batteries to work. Wine is battery. You give man four batteries and he much, much work."

It was hilarious and we laughed a lot. Just as we used to do. I wiped my eyes and looked around for Najib.

"I wonder where Najib is," I said.

"Najib?" Yassin looked at me with his eyes wide open, as if he had never heard the name before.

"Yes, Yassin. Najib, the electrician, who has been wiring up the mountain world for the past weeks."

"We are not waiting for Najib," he said, staring in fascination at the salt barrel on the table as if expecting it to suddenly do somersaults.

"Oh, are we not? What are we doing here then, just having a nice little chat?"

"I wanted you to meet Ali," Yassin said and turned round to the neighbouring table.

The thin man stabbed out his cigarette in the ashtray and grimaced his face into a hello.

"Who is that – one of your relatives?" I hissed at Yassin.

"No, he is not," he sulked. "He worked for my family. You can trust him."

"Like that overweight builder, you mean?"

Yassin shrugged his shoulders. I sighed. Had the builder really been such a bad recommendation, I thought? He had finished the job in time and he had done nearly everything he had promised. I turned my attention to Ali.

"*Bonjour,* Ali, *la bes*?" I said.

He bared his teeth at me.

"*La bes, Madame, bejer*?"

His voice was quiet and nasal. He was dressed in a spotless blue boiler suit. A green scarf was slung cheekily around his neck. A matching cap sat in immaculate position on his head. He stretched out his hand and I shook it, a weak hand that seemed to be reluctant to shake mine. I let go quickly. His nails were

146

manicured. I wondered if he had hennaed feet. A silly giggle threatened to burst out and destroy my image of a serious woman who knows what she wants.

"*Parlez-vous francais?*" I asked.

He shut his lips over his teeth, which made his skin stretch over his gaunt face. "*Berber.*"

I had almost expected it. I would have to rely on Yassin again to translate.

History is repeating itself.

I ignored it.

Yassin and Ali had a long conversation. After a while, I wondered if it was still concerning my electricity or if I should go for a walk on the beach and forget about it.

"He wants fifteen hundred dirham and he will finish in ten days. It is a good deal," Yassin turned to face me.

"How does he want to be paid?" I asked.

"Five hundred dirham now and the rest when he has finished."

There was nothing unusual about it. Not knowing if I would ever be able to find Najib and having this electrician conveniently at hand, with price tag attached and ready to go, I signed him on.

"He will go with you to buy what he needs for your house," Yassin said.

I jumped up. "Okay. Let's go to Tamraght."

"Ali doesn't want to go to Tamraght."

I sat down again. "He doesn't want to go to Tamraght? But that's where the builders' merchant is."

Yassin mumbled.

"Pardon?"

"Inezgane. He wants to go to Inezgane."

"Inezgane? He wants me to take him to Inezgane, south of Agadir, about thirty kilometres from here, when we can buy what he needs just ten minutes up the road?"

Yassin got up. "Maybe he gets a better deal there."

"If you say so. You are coming with us, Yassin?"

"No, I have got something to do." He did not look at me.

147

I should pull out. It did not sound right. At least I should insist on going to Tamraght. I did none of it, and soon I found myself driving to Inezgane with Ali on the passenger seat.

Ali unwrapped a strip of gum and popped it into his mouth. He started to chew vigorously. He folded the paper into a neat rectangle and placed it in the pocket of his boiler suit. A smell of mint mixed with smoker's breath floated past. I opened the window.

Inezgane was the souk for the building trade, a labyrinth of narrow dust tracks which were lined with stalls. Ali strode purposefully ahead. I followed his spear-minted scent, looking left and right. There were displays of ornate wall tiles with intricate patterns in green, red, yellow and blue, very delicate and shiny. There were floor tiles, thick and rough, made from cement, in faded shades of orange and red. Windows with green or yellow glass with tiny circular patterns, water taps from plain metal to luxurious fake-golden ones. There were stalls selling tools, cement, paints – and electrical bits. Ali ignored them all. Where was he taking me? To a dark corner of this souk, where he would rob me of my dirham and my credit card?

I wished Yassin was here.

Men rushed up and down; many were dressed in traditional *djellabas*. This was different to the souks I had been to with their colourful displays of vegetables and clothes and the scents of coriander and rose water. The builders' souk was dusty and smelled of cement. It had the dryness of a building site, which made me want to cough. There was no chitchat. Women were nowhere to be seen. It was a man's world, and it looked bleak and dull.

While I was trying to work out where we were in relation to my van Ali stopped in front of an inconspicuous looking shop. I nearly bumped into him.

We entered. Maybe Ali knew the shop owner; probably a member of his family. I prepared myself for a long exchange of greetings and enquiries.

Nothing like that happened.

"*Assalam alaikum.*"

A man popped up from behind, wearing a jade green *djellaba* and a white *Kufi* cap.

"*Alaikum assalam.*"

Ali handed over his shopping list, and the man disappeared into the depth of his stall. He rummaged through his stock, sending numerous boxes crashing to the floor and finally emerged, clutching a shoe box full of bits and bobs.

Ali arranged his face into an expression of importance, with his brows furrowed and his lips pressed together. After flipping through the box, he nodded approvingly.

The stallholder arranged his little cap, which had come adrift. He reached under his counter, brought out a small white plastic box and pushed it in front of me.

"*Madame*, this is a cut-out unit." He startled me with this unexpected address in English.

"You must not lose the guarantee card. No card – no electricity." He pulled out a piece of paper and thrust it in front of my eyes.

It was too close for me to focus on, but I made a mental note to keep it somewhere safe. Judging by the serious face of the stallholder, losing the guarantee card was a capital crime and the consequent punishment was probably that I would never ever be allowed to connect my house to the Moroccan electricity network or possibly even be expelled from the country.

The price I had to pay corresponded roughly with the estimate Ali had given in Yassin's cafe. Clutching the purchases, we left the shop. Ali led me back to the van, which seemed to be just around the corner.

We could have bought every single item back in Tamraght, in Ahmed's shop, I thought. So why come here to Inezgane?

A couple of months later I would understand, but then it would be too late.

We drove back to Taghazout. I gave Ali the deposit, and we agreed that he would start working at seven o'clock the next morning.

I left the spare key to the house with my friend Yassin.

"Could you please explain to Ali, that he must pick up the key from you every morning before he goes up to Taliouine, Yassin? I won't always be there."

"No problem, Kate. I will make sure of that."

"*Wacha, Madame*," Ali nodded. He retrieved the neatly folded paper from his pocket, unfolded it carefully and spat his chewed-out gum onto it. Then he hurled it onto the street and left.

The next morning, the electrician started to work at seven o'clock sharp. I began to relax. Maybe there would not be any major problems this time.

Chapter Twenty One

Eight o'clock in the morning, and there was no sign of Ali. I stood outside my house, warming my face in the early sun. I listened to the faint sound of the ocean waves. The air was already filled with the smell of bread baking in the argan fires.

Two figures ambled up the dust track, one vaguely familiar. I squinted and waited.

"My brother Abdullah." My friend Yassin took off his cap and wiped his forehead.

"*La bes, Madame.*"

Abdullah and I shook hands.

"Nice to see you up here, and so early in morning." I prompted my friend.

"Abdullah is a builder. He can give you good price." Yassin's eyes wandered across the hilly neighbourhood.

The two brothers disappeared into the house. I followed, grabbing a water bottle on the way. Abdullah looked around, discussing at length with Yassin what needed doing. I assumed.

"Twenty seven thousand."

I choked on the water I was drinking. Yassin took the bottle out of my hand and slapped my back.

We sat down in the shade of the terrace wall. After one hour, Abdullah had reduced his price to fifteen thousand. I was not prepared to pay more than twelve thousand.

From my terrace, I watched the brothers walk back down to Taghazout.

I remembered Cherifa's conversation with Yassin about not employing the village people. Maybe she was right; I should look amongst my neighbours for help. So far, no one had come forward and announced skills in the building trade, which was rather unusual as half of the local male population seemed to consist of builders.

I sat down outside my house, leaning against the wall.

"*Madame!*"

I opened my eyes. Hamza, Moulham's youngest son, stumbled across the field, nearly tripping over his feet as he hurried towards me. He was clutching his most precious possession: a small stereo radio. When Hamza had money, he would buy batteries and the radio would stay glued to his ear until the batteries ran out. However distorted, the sound the radio put a happy smile on his face.

Hamza was slightly disabled. His feet turned inwards and his legs moved awkwardly. His speech was slurred, and he stuttered. It was nearly impossible to understand him. Hamza had the sunny and innocent disposition of a child. He was ridiculously smooth-skinned and big-eyed which made his neatly trimmed moustache look like a disguise. A child dressed up as a man. A friendly child who laughed a lot and who was always prepared to help.

"*Madame – travailler?*"

I liked him.

"*Eyeh*, Hamza. Here, take this." I gave him a broom and a bucket and indicated him to clear every floor of the house from the remains of the builder's reign.

"*Madame, Madame, shokran*," Hamza shouted happily and staggered into the house to tackle the cement dust.

A lorry came chugging and puffing up the track sending pebbles and dust flying and chickens running. With a loud sigh, it collapsed in front of my house. Larbi jumped out of the cabin. Fondly, he patted his ancient Margius.

"*Madame* – good car. Brings *cimar* and *sable*, mountain no problem. Where I put?" He looked around.

"*Bonjour*, Larbi. Just dump everything in front of the house."

As if they weighed no more than cushions, he unloaded numerous fifty-kilo cement bags from his lorry. A press of a button, and the bed of the lorry tilted with a screech, tipping a pyramid of golden sand in front of the house.

"*Safi*, *Madame*." Larbi sank down onto the ground in the shadow of his vehicle and pulled a small bottle of water out of the pocket of his jacket.

"Would you like oranges?" I asked, holding two out to him.

"*Merci*, *Madame* – you have cigarette?" He grinned.

Hamza appeared. Without being asked, he started to carry the cement bags into the house. He was strong for a fragile looking man.

I joined Larbi on the ground. I had gone to Aourir on my own to order building materials. I had walked up and down the line of lorries until I found Larbi. We continued our negotiations where we had been interrupted by my neighbour Yassin that day and agreed a deal satisfying for both of us.

We smoked, watching Hamza.

"Hamza good boy," Larbi said.

Hamza shovelled his way through three tons of sand, filling buckets and carrying them into the house. The buckets leaked and fine trails of sand led to my front door. Sooner or later, every bucket in Morocco leaks.

"Yes, very good," I agreed.

Larbi had finished his rest and jumped up.

"*Madame* – must work."

"Yes, me too," I laughed.

He climbed into his cabin and started the engine. With a bang and a deafening rattling noise, the lorry came to life.

"*A la prochaine*!" Larbi shouted.

The engine almost drowned his voice.

I could still make out a faint chugging sound five minutes later, when the lorry arrived in Taghazout.

Ali the electrician did not show up that day. My friend Yassin, on the other hand, arrived a second time in Taliouine. He was accompanied by his uncle. His uncle was a builder and his price was thirteen thousand dirham, but without painting the walls inside or outside. I wondered how many more relatives Yassin was going to bring up the hill.

It was Wednesday, and after his eager start on Sunday morning, I had not seen Ali again and was not sure what to do about it. I did not think it necessary at the time to agree that the ten days of work we had estimated would be consecutive. At this rate, he would only be finished in two years time.

Wednesday was souk day in Aourir, and I set off in the morning to stock up with fresh vegetables and fruit, maybe buy some fresh chicken or fish.

To simply translate souk as a market is an understatement. A souk is a spectacle, a feast for the senses, a firework of colours and scents. It is more than shopping; it is indulgence, seduction, a special treat.

Excitedly, I pulled off the road in Aourir and parked on the dusty surface, squeezing in between battered vans, which had brought the mountain people down for their weekly day out. Women wrapped in brightly coloured fabrics rushed past, clutching baskets and bags. I zigzagged across the busy road towards the souk and saw Ali the split second before he sank down behind a dilapidated taxi. Our eyes met. Like in slow motion, he ducked and then was hidden. I sprinted and literally grabbed him by his collar.

"Why don't you work?" I asked in French, which by now I was sure he understood.

He indicated that he had been up to Taliouine. The house had been locked. So he had gone back to Taghazout and on to Aourir.

"The key is in Yassin's café."

"*Wacha, Madame.*" Ali's eyes darted around.

Not for one minute did I believe that he had been up to the village. More likely, he had not been able to find a lift in the morning and decided not to bother. And where had he been the two days before? Same story, same excuse? But there was no easy way of finding out with our limited possibilities to communicate.

I left him alone - what else could I do? – and threw myself into the pleasures of the souk.

Once a week, the vast empty place between the main road and the ocean transformed into a kaleidoscope of colours, smells and sounds as if touched by a magic wand in the night. The merchants arrived at sunrise, covering nearly every inch of the dusty square with plastic sheets or blankets onto which they heaped their products, leaving narrow pathways for the customers. Fruit and vegetables were arranged into elaborate displays. Oranges and lemon were piled into pyramids. Carrots and turnips were stacked like walls of firewood. Potatoes and beetroots were poured out of crates into uneven heaps. There was an air of boundless abundance.

My eyes were feeding on the colours. The bright spring sun was hot, yet still clear and free of the heat haze of the months to come, and illuminated the different colours: the reds of tomatoes, strawberries and peppers, the orange of satsumas, pumpkins and oranges, the greens of lettuces, beans and artichokes. Even the brown shades of potatoes were glowing like rare gems and so did the dark beetroots. There were aubergine, courgette and peppers in all shades of red, green and yellow, which made me think of Ratatouille. There were leeks, celery and onions. Red onions. There were no white onions in Morocco, and I always wondered why not. Garlic bulbs were stripped off their papery skin, vulnerable and exposed, like exotic flowers.

The air was scented with the aroma of oranges which were cut into wedges by the sellers and thrust into passer-bys' hands for testing. The Moroccan people were very meticulous shoppers. Everything was sampled first if possible. Potatoes were chosen carefully, which could take a long time. The slightest mark and back they went onto the heap.

The souk was a feast for my senses. It made my mouth water and lifted my spirits. The pungent smell of mint and coriander mingled with the oranges. Fresh herbs are vital ingredients in Moroccan daily life, as essential as bread. They are sold in enormous bunches. Wrapped in torn bits of yellowing newspaper they make their way to nearly every dwelling, to flavour tea and *tajines*.

Merchants, who sold the same goods, clustered together. Seven displays of oranges here, eight sheets of beans over there, ten tomato sellers grouped in the far corner. There were no women amongst the sellers, but more women than men amongst the shoppers.

"The way to meet girls is either on the bus or in the souk," my friend Yassin once explained to me.

I watched the younger women, their hair modestly hidden under colourful scarves, and found their eyes not only scrutinizing the vegetables but also secretly scanning the crowd and sending out coy signals.

One part of the souk was reserved for the sale of dates, raisins and nuts, dried peas and beans. There were pyramids of green and black olives and enormous jars of pickled lemons. Some stalls were selling spices, which were arranged on big trays: powdery mounds of ochre, cinnamon, brown, terracotta and yellow – the warmest assortment of colours one could imagine.

I loved to buy spices. It was so comfortingly old fashioned. The seller concocted mixtures for certain dishes, from chicken *tajine* and lamb couscous to grilled fish, whatever meal was on the customer's menu. He would take a small brown paper bag and an ancient looking wooden spoon – both items reminded me of my old wooden toy corner shop, where I used to scoop up dried peas and bag them for my long since perished dolls. He would begin with a tiny scoop of yellow, add a bigger one of terracotta, a soupcon of ochre and so on, until the mixture was right. He would hand over the bag in return for a small amount of dirham.

With the bag of spices, there was often a freebie, like a cinnamon stick or a few almonds, which was very kind. If you liked the almonds, you could buy more from his brother, whom he was only too happy to introduce you to. His brother would also offer you a free sample of his peanuts and walnuts, tell you that all of his seven children were sick and you would end up, with tears in your eyes, buying a kilo of peanuts and half a kilo of walnuts you would never eat, so he could buy medicine for his children.

Nearly all merchants in Aourir had seven sick children. Or at least they said they had.

There was a non-food part of the market, where pots and pans, carpets and blankets, toiletries and clothes were being sold. The all day outfit for the Berber women was an ankle-length cotton nightie – at least, it was worn as a nightdress in Europe. The Berber women wore it with leggings underneath and topped with a headscarf. And it did not look like a nightie at all.

Souks are not only about scents and colours; they are also about noises. The noise level in Aourir was fantastic. Goods were offered in a fast Berber staccato, each seller trying to outdo the competitors. There was a high level of excitement as the competition was fierce. The pressure to sell possibly all his merchandise was enormous for every man who had a family to look after.

There was a storyteller, narrating via microphone at a breathless speed to a rapt audience of young and old, male and female.

There was the panic stricken screeching of hens about to enter the decapitating and de-feathering machine, which was going to turn them into lumpy ingredients for the next *tajine*.

And of course, there was the relentless chatter of people. As my friend Yassin explained, the weekly souk is more a social outing than simply a shopping trip. People usually come down from the mountain villages, by donkey, cart or bus, bringing news from family members to the ones who have settled down here by the sea and picking up the latest gossip to take back to the hills to spread it amongst the ones who had to stay behind.

A souk is like a beehive, buzzing with activity. There is a continuous coming and going, and a never ceasing hum fills the air. I love it.

In the beginning, when I was new in this area and considered to be no more than a tourist, a fool, a pushover, sent by Allah to fill the market sellers' pockets with money, I felt hassled and uncomfortable. Shopping was like running the gauntlet, and I loathed it. There was no friendly word, and I was charged at least twice as much as the local people. I was fought over by sellers, literally torn into pieces. After a while, I established some contacts. People recognised me from the week before, and the word travelled that I was building a house in the hills. It had a higher esteem than "building a house by the sea" as it was more of a challenge, physically and emotionally, because the mountain people were considered to be a very close knit community. People I had never seen before stopped me in the souk, telling me that they knew about my house, congratulating me and wishing me good luck. This network of communication without the help of mod cons like telephone, television or radio was rather impressive.

I am proud to say that nowadays visiting the souk AND doing my shopping is a doddle for me. I test and compare, I complain and haggle, and I refuse and agree. I can see through the tricks when they are played on me and protest which only earns me respect. One day, when my Berber has picked up I might even be able to chitchat with the other women and then return to my village in the hills, laden with news, and all the Cherifas, Minas and Yasminas will be coming to my house for tea, eager to hear the latest gossip.

Weighed down with fruit and vegetables I left the souk. I had also bought a nightie, which reminded me, colour wise, of the hills surrounding my village. I was apprehensive of wearing it, partly, because to me it would always be a nightdress, and partly, because I feared giggles from the other women when I paraded around dressed as "one of them". Due to its brownish pattern, though, I might completely blend into the backdrop of the Atlas Mountains and nobody would notice me wearing it. Or I could simply give it to Nashiema.

Ali was still hanging around more or less in the same place. As he did not seem to have anything else to do, I offered him a lift up to Taliouine.

"*Oho*," the electrician declined, pointing at the hot sun and fanning his face with his little hand.

"Okay, tomorrow, then. *Ghsaad*."

Ali nodded. "*Insha'allah*."

Insha'allah. There was nothing more to say. I crossed the road and loaded the shopping into my van.

Chapter Twenty Two

When I checked *le parking,* I found the concrete slab covered with a fine layer of dust. The surface was dry. I rushed back to my van, threw books, cups, pots and pans into the cupboards and was soon bumping along the path into the village, leaving behind a herd of disappointed goats. We had become friends.

"I'll come and see you," I shouted out of the window. I had come to like the way my organic waste was appreciated and re-used.

I could not wait to install myself next to my house. I swayed and swerved and spun up the steep track, trying to avoid jam-pan-sized potholes. My van was as suitable for off road trips as a pair of high heels. I dreaded the first rain, which most certainly was going to leave the path impassable. Luckily, there was hardly any rain in this area...

I pulled into my corner of Moulham's field and reversed into *le parking.* My enthusiasm switched off with the engine. I stared around me. Apart from the view out of my front window, there was a grey breeze block wall to my left, which belonged to my unknown neighbour's house. There was a grey breeze block wall to my right, which belonged to my house. Between my parking and the house was the path leading up to Yasmina's house in the back: another grey breeze block wall. I felt closed in, claustrophobic.

Yasmina appeared to sweep the path while talking to herself. I watched her through the net curtains of my side window, her head not more than half a metre from mine. From now on, I would have to listen to Yasmina's clucking all day. I wondered if I could live with it and realised that I preferred the company of the goats.

Yasmina swept her way back into her house. Her young son Mohamed appeared, a shy boy with a friendly smile. He was carrying a tiny puppy. In the shelter of the path, he tried to pull its leg off. The puppy cried. I rapped on the window. Mohamed jumped and ran into the house. The puppy hobbled away, yelping, and I felt sick.

I left my van, looking for the comfort of the warm sunlight.

Moulham came bouncing down the path from his house, laden with freshly baked bread and his son Bilal in tow.

"You have work," he said.

Bilal loitered in the background and gave me a wry smile. Moulham pointed at his son.

"Bilal very good. Very fast." Moulham thrust the bread into my arms which smelled of *baksheesh*.

Bilal was even smaller than Moulham, if that was at all possible. His clothes, his shoes – everything reminded me of a twelve-year-old boy. Everything but his face which looked nearly as old as Moulham's.

"Bilal very good price," Moulham continued, offering his ancient looking son to me like a sheep.

For one hundred and twenty dirham a day Bilal would plaster the whole inside of the house within three weeks. As he needed a dogsbody to mix cement and clean up after him, Moulham suggested Hamza at fifty dirham a day.

I could have hugged them but restrained myself to shaking first Moulham's, then Bilal's hand which made the latter giggle with embarrassment. Hamza joined us, brush in his hand, and uttered a string of happy sounds. A millstone had been taken off me. It saved me looking around for labourers, and I was supporting the neighbourhood economy, even though it was not exactly Cherifa's branch of the family.

To celebrate the fact that he had managed to install two of his unemployed sons with me Moulham invited me for tea to his house.

"*Madame, azih.*" He waved me to follow him.

Bilal trundled off across the field.

I was excited and honoured because so far I had not been invited to Moulham's house. The entrance to his property was marked by the customary metal door. An intriguing wrought iron pattern weaved across the metal surface and was painted in bright blue, brown and black. Moulham pushed the door open and invited me in. A path led up to the main entrance of the house, past a small field, barren and bare except for one lone argan tree. A door on the right side led into Hamza's room, as Moulham explained.

We entered the inner courtyard. It was a typical Berber house, large though, with five doors leading off the yard into rooms.

A tiny old woman appeared. She was as elfin as Moulham.

"Aicha. *Femme,*" he introduced his wife.

Aicha put her hand on my arm, said many things which I did not understand and gave a toothless smile. Moulham shooed her away and gave me a tour of the elves' dwelling, pulling me in and out of narrow windowless rooms, each sparsely furnished with a mattress or a cupboard. There was Aicha's room, a kitchen, a spare room and Moulham's room.

"Mohamed. Melikha." Moulham said and showed me the last room, where yet another son lived, with his wife and two sons. Curiously, I looked inside the small room that housed four people. On the mattress sat a young woman, Melikha, playing with a large round baby. I had seen her several times before, each time of which she had greeted me with a warm smile. She had huge dark eyes, almost oversized compared to her straight nose and the curved lips. She looked as striking as Nashiema, without being coy. Melikha was straight forward and open. Her voice was husky, and I liked to hear her laugh out loud, which she often did, mostly when she was playing with the children.

She carried her baby around in a sling all day. All the women here did. There were no prams or pushchairs. I wish more European women would follow this example of carrying their babies strapped to their bodies instead of dumping the poor things in prams. Melikha's dresses all had a right-angled cut under the sleeves. It took me a while to understand its purpose. When Melikha's baby needed feeding, she would just lift the fabric and latch him onto her breast. It still amazes me to see women in Morocco breastfeeding their babies, wherever and whenever it is necessary: in the street, in the market or on the back of a van. They don't feel inhibited about exposing their breasts in public to feed and I have never seen a man stare. It is very difficult for me to understand how it works in this otherwise so closed society, where women have to hide their bare arms, ankles and hair in order not to tempt men. The only explanation I found is that the lactating breast is given a different name to de-sexualise it and that it is an offence to stare at a woman breastfeeding. Still, it is hard to believe that it should work as easily as that.

How much we could learn from the Berber women! Sadly, they believe they should follow the western example. One day Nashiema showed me a bag she had been given by a representative of a well-known company. It contained many feel-good things for Nashiema, bribes really, to make her use the formula milk, which nestled at the bottom of the goody-bag like an ugly poisonous snake.

"*Oho*, Nashiema," I said.

She had never seen me angry and nearly dropped the bag. I grabbed the formula tin.

"This is no good. No good for babies. You must breastfeed. Only breast milk is good."

Nashiema was stunned and I could see her innocent view of the world wobble. I don't think it shattered. More likely, she thought I had lost my marbles judging by the bewildered expression on her face.

Melikha lifted her well-nourished baby off the bed and swung him onto her hip. She came to shake my hand.

"Mohamed." She pointed at her son and laughed.

I held his fleshy soft hand for a while. He gurgled. His hand felt good in mine, the way he grabbed my fingers and wouldn't let go. Melikha watched me all the time, laughing and talking. I wanted to sit with her on the mattress and play with her baby, but I was Moulham's guest and when he indicated me to follow him into his room I had to peel Mohamed's hand off my thumb.

Nobody seemed to disapprove of me following Moulham into his room. There was no privacy in these rooms anyway, as they were all open to the court yard. But still, I was a woman, and this was a traditional male dominated society. Maybe visiting the village boss was an exception, or maybe Moulham was simply considered to be past any sexual activities due to his age.

Moulham was completely self-sufficient, making tea and serving bread and Amlou without the help of a female.

"Good. *Mezyan.*" I said, pointing at the sign of his autonomy.

Moulham poured tea into the glasses and handed one over to me.

"*Moi, je fait ca.* No woman." He waggled his index finger. "Aicha, Aicha – Moulham, Moulham."

I was pleased to see a bit of equality between men and women in Taliouine.

We chatted for a while in our incomprehensible language mix, then ran out of subjects and stared at the whitewashed walls. I watched a giant ant rushing up and down looking for a way out. After the customary three glasses of mint tea, I got up to leave.

"*Shokran.*" I said and stepped into the yard.

There was no sign of Aicha or Melikha. Moulham accompanied me to his front door.

When I walked back to the van, I felt contented that Moulham's family respected me. Life was looking brighter. My house was getting on, I was employing local people and I felt increasingly accepted into this village.

I had no idea that a fierce competition had begun, with me being the first prize.

Chapter Twenty Three

The next day I met Melikha again.

When I woke up, I could not see anything. For the first time since I arrived, Taliouine was in the clouds. I felt weightless, enclosed and oppressed. There was an unpleasant feeling of isolation. I saw nothing, heard nothing and the air smelled of dampness and rubbish. It was dull and reminded me of cold autumn mornings in the hills of Garfagnana in Italy. Most of all, there was no view, only cotton-woollen murkiness below.

A shadow moved, and I was pleased to identify it to be the electrician busily running in and out of the house. I had nearly forgotten about him. Luckily, he did not find fog a reason not to come to work.

"*Bonjour*," I shouted, entering the building site.

"*La bes, Madame.*" The electrician flicked a speck of dust off his boiler suit. A faint scent of chewed spearmint hung in the air. He was holding on to a screwdriver. His eyes lingered with unveiled disgust on my dirty shirt and track suit bottoms - my outfit for work.

I found Bilal and Hamza crouching on the roof terrace.

"*Madame*," Hamza shrieked, jumping up from his squatting position and clapping his hands.

Bilal grinned, took his baseball cap off and put it on again.

We nodded at each other, indicating mutual sympathy and satisfaction over our working arrangement.

I was pleased to notice that they had taken matters in their own hands and were preparing the terrace for plastering. I rolled up my sleeves and crouched down to help clean the floor.

"*Oho, Madame.*" Life shot into Bilal. He jumped and pulled me off the floor.

Hamza giggled.

I shook Bilal's hands off.

"Now guys, this has to be clear. I like working with my hands, and I will help building my house. And you are not going to stop me, just because it is not custom in your village. *Wacha*?"

I couldn't image that the two of them had really understood, but they nodded.

"*Wacha, Madame.*"

We all crouched back down to tackle the floor of the terrace.

The fog dried up, and the day turned out to be hot and sunny. The floor of the terrace was cleared. There was nothing for me to do. Bilal had started plastering the walls of the terrace, and I grew bored of watching Hamza mixing cement and Ali sorting through the box of bits.

I walked off, following the path in front of my house towards the deserted part at the back of the village. The dusty path took me deep into a lost world of traditional stone houses, most of which were derelict, with collapsed walls and ceilings, yet occasionally still sporting an elaborate front door. Accessible parts of those dwellings were used to deposit rubbish. The privacy of some crumbling rooms was used for toilets.

People had moved out of the old stone houses and into the more recent breezeblock constructions, which were ugly, but more comfortable. No more scorpions nesting undetected between the stones; the whitewashed breezeblock walls were smooth and easy to keep clean. They would also withstand extreme weather conditions like heavy rain, sandstorms and drought.

The village was surrounded by small fields which mostly belonged either to Moulham or Cherifa. However, there were more inhabitants to the village than the two families at war.

Abdul, for example, owned a large *epicerie* in Taghazout. A food stall was a profitable business, and Abdul was the only man in the Taliouine, who could afford a second floor. He also was one of the few who owned a vehicle, a tatty rattling Ford Transit. He offered lifts up and down the mountains for five dirham each way, and he had two wives. There were a few more families - their houses were dotted around the edge of the village - but except for an occasional *la bes* or a smile, they did not appear to want much contact with either the families at war or with me.

My eyes followed the paths leading into the mountains, and I imagined the places I would get to if I one day locked my door and set off. I was fascinated by the Atlas Mountains, by their vastness and wilderness. The fact that I was standing on the edge of this enormous range, filled me with awe. The hill top villages were nearly invisible and vegetation virtually non-existent. It was barren and sparing with colours and features, almost hostile - nothing like the colourful brightness of the South of France, which I loved. Yet, something drew me towards these mountains: the sheer supremacy of nature and its coarse beauty, like the rough handsomeness of men, who spent most of their lives outdoors.

In the late afternoon, I retreated to my favourite place: the stony hills opposite the village, uninhabited and peaceful, were a perfect place to think, reflect and watch the sunset.

It was there where I met Melikha. She smiled at me and greeted me with the customary kisses between women: three on my left cheek, one on my right. Her hair smelled faintly of wood fire. Baby Mohamed bounced and gurgled happily in his sling on her hip. Melikha was accompanied by four of the village children. They were collecting argan wood. I offered to help and learned that all the thorns had to be taken off the twigs. It was painful and arduous work, but it was the only wood available in the hills.

Melikha and the children taught me Berber words and, with eruptions of hilarious laughter, imitated my accent. When enough wood was collected, Melikha turned it into a huge parcel. She grabbed some rubbery leaves and placed them on her head, swung the parcel on top and set off for home, swaying under the weight of the wood and the tubby baby on her hip.

"Melikha, let me help you," I said and stretched out my arms.

She refused and smiled at me, revealing the whitest most beautiful teeth I had ever seen, like an advertisement for expensive dentures. They illuminated her fine tanned face. Her dark eyes sparkled even though she was nearly breaking under the weight she had to carry.

All the way back to the village, Melikha and the children were singing songs from the mountains, their voices travelling out into the post-sunset sky.

The sound of drumming drifted across from our village.

Darkness was slowly descending on us. The village would soon be dark; there was no moon to illuminate it. Fires would be lit instead of candles which were a precious and expensive commodity. The village people would sit around their fires for a while and then go to bed. Here in Taliouine, I felt very much in tune with nature, and it came perfectly naturally to me to go to bed when it was dark and get up with the sun in the morning. What confusing thing electricity was for the human body, when days were artificially prolonged and entertainment came via television and radio instead of listening to nature or conversing with other people.

The sound of drumming grew louder the nearer we came to my house. Sitting on the ground with their backs leaning against the wall was the family at war, for once peacefully united. Cherifa, Moulham and Yassin were playing the tam tams, the Moroccan ceramic drums, while the various daughters, daughters-in-law and their children had gathered around to sing and dance. With a scream, the children left our side and joined the dancers. I sat down. Melikha carried her parcel home, then returned and sat down by my side, placing a sleepy Mohamed in

170

my arm. His soft hand enclosed my thumb. The warm body grew heavier as the little man drifted off, his peaceful face resting against my chest. Three candles had been stuck into the sand and lit, their flicker moving to the rhythm of the drums.

It ended as spontaneously as it had started. The drums became silent, the dancers stopped. The candles were blown out and stowed away for the next time. Everybody went home. I stayed sitting for a long time wondering if I had only imagined it, while trying to hold on to the patch of warmth Mohamed's body had left behind.

Although no major crisis occurred, things did not continue to run as smoothly as they had done for a few days. My workers' enthusiasm cooled down quickly, and the electrician did not make an appearance at all.

After an initial period of swift plastering Bilal slowed down to half his speed. One day he plastered the bedroom ceiling except *metro*, a square metre. It was half the amount of daily work he had done before. Bilal was paid by the day. By taking it easy he actually would earn more money.

Hamza did not do much else all day than standing around and watching his brother. Leaning on his spate, he waited for Bilal to demand more cement. Between mixing cement were hundreds of jobs, which needed to be done. When I asked him to sweep the floor or to help me carry stones outside, he would smile at me and nod.

"*Wacha, Madame.*" After that, he would turn his attention back to Bilal and ignore me. He had developed the habit of knowing everything better. His favourite word was *oho*, no, accompanied by an expressive waggling of the index finger. As soon as I picked up a spate, tried my hand at plastering or started a sentence, Hamza would wake out of his lethargy and drive me up the wall with a loud finger-waggling *oho*. Bilal only grinned goofily on those occasions. I had to ask Moulham for help.

Hamza was not able to count and the cement mixtures varied in texture, which was clearly visible when slapped onto the wall. I tried to teach him: for every bucket of sand he took he

171

had to give me a stone. For every bucket of water he used he had to give me a stick. The mixtures became more even.

One evening Moulham brought fresh fish up from Taghazout, *Asmisa*, and invited me to share a *tajine*. It was kind of him and it would give me the chance to speak about Hamza. I took biscuits and chocolate for him and Aicha and a bottle of coke. It was a lovely evening. Aicha, Moulham and I were sitting by candlelight, eating the delicious fish *tajine* and listening to the waves far below crashing onto the rocks. It was peaceful, and I was happy that the two old people offered me their hospitality. Aicha was giggling, taking my hand from time to time. Moulham promised to have a word with Hamza.

He saw me out into a moonless night and whispered, "*Donnez-moi l'argent!*"

What did he mean? Money for what? For the fish? For his *litros*? For his family? I was already employing two of his sons, who seemed to end up costing more money than necessary. And how much? Ten? One hundred? One thousand? I pretended not to have heard him, bid him goodnight and left.

I was upset. As soon as I felt a budding affection from the side of the villagers, something happened which threw me back. It dawned on me that I would probably never know in this village, maybe even in this country, if people really liked me or my money, if they invited me because of myself or because they were calculating the favour they would ask in return for the invitation. It was a depressing thought. All the smiling faces, the invitations to tea, the baking of bread for me – was there one amongst them who liked me, or were they all thinking of the advantage they might be able to take of me?

I knew that I would have to share what I had with my neighbours up to a point, and I was prepared to do that. But I also wanted to be liked. I wanted to be invited for a meal because it was nice to be with me.

Well, maybe it wasn't. I walked back to my van. I could see myself turning from a lonely traveller into a lonely dweller.

For the first time, the night sky was dark and cloudy. Very unlikely to have rain, I thought.

The next day rain poured down like from buckets and turned the village into a dreary place, exposing poverty, rubbish and barrenness. Rivulets of rainwater ran down the mud paths and through the dwellings. Water leaked through the roofs. As there hardly ever was a lot of rain, nobody was equipped for it.

Nevertheless, the rain was much appreciated by my neighbours.

Melikha knocked on my window and waved me to follow her to the edge of the village, where the villagers had surrounded the vast new government-built cistern. Once it had filled up with rain water, the women would not have to walk the donkeys to the well for a while. Feeling raindrops on my skin was a strange sensation. Having escaped much of the rain in the past seven years, I found the cool wetness unpleasant.

Little rivers of water came rushing down the hillside, heading for the cistern – and passed it.

The channels, which had been dug and concreted to feed the water into the opening of the cistern, were stubbornly ignored in favour of the natural geography of the hillside. The disappointed village people tried to divert the rivulets by building dams with stones and branches, but most of the water still flowed on towards Taghazout.

It was often like this in Morocco. Money was made available, in this case to build a cistern, but sadly, the necessary expertise was lacking. The cistern would remain useless like this for ages.

I spent the grey day in my grey *parking* staring alternately at the grey walls of my house on one side and the grey walls of my unknown neighbour's house on the other, feeling depressed and misplaced. I watched the track turn into a small river and cut me off from the world outside the village. I could have stopped there and then and left. I fled into a daydream of getting back to Spain and driving into Gibraltar, heading for Tesco and the nearest pub. I would also pick up a roast chicken at Safeway's, and a lettuce, and a strawberry cheesecake for desert. And a bottle of wine! And a newspaper! Then I would drive to my favourite place, Catalan Bay, and have a feast. I would spend the night right there, and in the morning I would be woken up by the screeching of the seagulls. My mouth watered, and I broke into a happy smile or rather a daft grin, as it turned out when I caught my reflection in the mirror.

A knock on the door brought me back to Taliouine. It was Cherifa. She smiled at me and held out two loaves of freshly baked bread. I thanked her, but could not help feeling as if the two rivalling families were trying to outdo each other to win the prize, which was me, the golden calf. I ate the bread anyway, because there was nothing else to eat. I had planned to go to Taghazout, but because of the rain, I had decided to stay.

Soon my stomach started to rumble and churn, and I felt sick. I remembered what Yassin had told me about Cherifa's witchcraft. Was I slowly being poisoned? Surely, they wouldn't poison a golden calf, would they?

DOWN TOWARDS THE SEA

Chapter Twenty Four

The rain passed and with it my dark mood. The next day brought bright warm sunshine; everything looked more cheerful and I had new energy. The surface of the track was drying up. It had remained passable.

I had been in the country for a while, and my permit to stay would run out in four weeks. It was time to apply for a prolongation of my visa which involved filling in a stack of forms and undertaking numerous trips to town halls and police stations. It was French bureaucracy at its most intimidating. I asked Bilal and Hamza to take a holiday, locked my house and set off to tackle yet another milestone.

The first thing to do was to open a bank account. The Moroccan government requested from applicants a proof of financial autonomy. An account with a local bank, holding a deposit of dirham was sufficient. I drove into Agadir and entered the Wafa bank.

It was all easy and straightforward. After filling in a minimum of forms, I handed my visa card over to the woman behind the counter. She debited my card with twenty thousand dirham, which were going to go into my brand new account.

"My bank account in Morocco. . . " I murmured several times, listening in embarrassment, yet with delight, to the sound

175

of smugness bouncing off the marble walls. It was like "My chateau in the Loire..." or "My yacht in the Med..." I was excited, as it was another proof that I was not merely a tourist in this country. A faint beep announced that the monetary transaction had been completed. Everything was so unproblematic that I started to worry where the snag was.

"*Attendez, s'il vous plait, Madame.*" The woman adjusted her headscarf and disappeared.

Here we go, I thought. Something major has happened and I was not going to have a bank account with a Moroccan bank. I waited and wondered. Maybe I had no money left on my English account?

After ten minutes, the woman returned. Her high heels, barely visible under a pink *djellaba*, were click-clacking over shiny floor tiles. She smiled and waved me to follow her into a sterile air-conditioned room at the back of the bank.

"*Madame – Monsieur le directeur.*" She introduced me to the bank manager, a young man, who jumped up from behind a plain metal desk, which was laden with piles of paper.

"*Bonjour, Madame*, sit down please. My name is Lyazid."

He pointed at a dated armchair in front of the desk.

Was it his family name? Or his first name?

"*Madame*, unfortunately it is not possible to open an account by paying in dirham. You need to have a foreign currency and it has to be cash. Then we will convert into dirham – *et voilà* – it goes into your new account."

"I have no cash other than dirham, *Monsieur*."

I was sure that I was not carrying large amounts of foreign currencies with me, in fact, I was pretty sure that I did not have any foreign money left, having bribed the odd policeman in this country with my last pesetas.

"*Madame* must have." His dark eyes searched my face. "Pounds, French franc – or maybe dollars?"

I smiled weakly.

"*Madame, s'il-vous-plait, cherchez*! Maybe you will find, even if it is only a small note," Monsieur Lyazid implored me.

It seemed ridiculous. Why did it have to be a foreign currency, and why cash? I searched my purse, my documents with little hope. But then, nestling inside my driving licence like an ancient sweet wrapper, I found a long forgotten five-pound note. How it got there, I did not know.

With a regretful smile, I pulled it out. Monsieur Lyazid would probably be in fits of laughter. Five pounds only.

But nothing like this happened. He jumped up once more, grabbing the note from my hands."This is absolutely sufficient," he cried.

Shortly afterwards, I walked out of the bank, a proud holder of an account with a Moroccan bank, with a balance of eighty dirham in credit.

I couldn't even begin to understand how my deposit of twenty thousand dirham had been refused in favour of the dirham equivalent of five pounds. It was part of Morocco's charm, not to be able to understand. It was not the first time, and it was certainly not going to be the last.

Back in the town hall of Taghazout, I nonchalantly waved my brand new bank statement in front of the clerk's eyes. He ignored it and dumped a bundle of forms onto the desk.

"Fill it in, make three copies, then come back," he said and swept me out of the town hall in his usual efficient manner.

Three copies? That would make about eighty pages altogether. For a permit to remain ninety more days in this country. Almost one page for each day. It seemed rather a lot of paperwork to me.

The next day I had to leave Bilal alone, because I needed to get some timber for shelves and shuttering. I did not expect much work to be done during my absence.

The electrician had not arrived by the time I left, and I wondered if I would ever see him again. My friend Yassin had ordered his brother Mohamed to accompany me to Tamraght to find a carpenter he knew. Another commission was beckoning and Mohamed had to make sure I wasn't spoiling it by straying off to a different carpenter. Mohamed was an unusually tall and strongly-built Moroccan who hardly ever smiled. I knew from Yassin that Mohamed had a son with a German woman who was living in Berlin, but Mohamed did never talk about it.

In Aourir, we separated shortly, for me to have my photos taken for the visa, and for Mohamed to do some shopping.

I endured the process of being photographed with patience, although I had to remain in the same position for a long time, until camera and photographer were finally ready for the shot. My smile was frozen by that time. It was hot and sticky. My eyes were half shut and my hair plastered to my head. Sweaty patches had appeared on my shirt. I looked like a halfwit in need of a bath. The prolongation would be rejected just on grounds of my photo.

Embarrassed, I stumbled out of the small stall into Aourir's street. It was hot and busy. Aourir always smelled of engine oil and paint, of hot metal and diesel. It was the artisan centre of this area, with hundreds of stalls lining the main road, from car repair places to carpenters, from welders to bike mechanics. Today another scent lingered in the air: the odour of sheep.

I followed the sound of bleating to the crossroads, where a crowd of men had gathered. There was a general handling and fondling of the animals. Weight, age and dirham were discussed with serious faces. It was like a sheep market. Once a sheep was bought, it was taken by its legs and thrown on top of a lorry. Or into the boot of a car.

"They sail ships," Mohamed said behind me, back from his shopping spree.

I turned round. "They sail ships?"

"Yes, they sail ships. For *Aid el Kebir*."

Aid el Kebir is one of the major feasts of the Muslim calendar, held two months and ten days after the end of Ramadan. It celebrates Abraham's willingness to obey Allah to the extent of sacrificing his son Isaac. Instead of a son, every family slaughters a sheep, if they can afford it. *Aid el Kebir* is a family gathering, and it was merely a week to go until the whole of the country would come to a standstill to celebrate. That was the reason why "they sell sheep" today in Aourir.

178

We drove up and down Aourir but could not find the carpenter anywhere.

He was probably out, buying a sheep.

I dropped my plan to acquire wood and Mohamed off at Taghazout and returned to Taliouine.

As expected, hardly any work had been done on my house. Bilal had not even finished the ceiling of the landing. He and Hamza were loitering around, trying to appear busy and avoiding guiltily my eyes.

Sternly I said, "*Imiksimik*." This meant as much as 'I am not happy that only little work was done today.'

"*Oho, oho*." Hamza waggled his finger. He gave me a long explanation, which I did not understand.

I entered the first floor bedroom and found the raffia carpet rolled out and my pink blanket crumpled up. The stale smell of sleep hung in the air.

"*Madame, atei,*" Bilal tried to pacify me.

I accepted his invitation. I was curious to see how Bilal lived and also to get to know Fatima better, Bilal's wife.

Fatima looked about twenty years younger than Bilal and was much taller than him. She appeared more intelligent than the whole village together and had a sense of humour. She laughed often, not the giggly hysterical high-pitched shrieks most of the village women favoured, but in a melodious and quieter way.

Bilal's house was next to Moulham's, or rather an extension of his. We entered through an ornate brown metal door into a minute courtyard where two doorways led into two small rooms. It was the sparsest of habitats I had seen in Taliouine so far. Fatima and Bilal did not even have mattresses, only blankets on the ground – a bedstead, which they shared with their children.

Rachid and his sister Mina were watching me from a distance. They were holding hands, and each had a finger in its mouth. They were tiny fragile children, like pixies: a gene in the family.

"Rachid – *mezyan*," Fatima explained. "Mina – *oho*." She waggled her outstretched hand and looked upset.

Indeed, Mina, a wisp of a child, did not look healthy. Her tummy was protruding like a football, and she was never out playing with the other children.

A brand new stone wall was being built in the yard to create a kitchen corner. The cement was still wet. When was Bilal doing that? In the night, in the dark? Or when I went off to Agadir or Aourir? While Hamza was having a nap on my carpet under my pink blanket? Where did the cement come from? I knew that my possessions were considered to be a gift to the village by Allah, and when I was not looking after them, everyone was entitled to take his share out of Allah's generous present. I did not mind at all. I was happy to be able to help my neighbours to improve the standard of their living.

Fatima pulled me over to the cistern, which was brimming with fresh water. They had not been able to afford the water lorry for a long time. Secretly, I resolved to employ Bilal as long as I could afford it, even if he slowed down to snail speed.

We shared tea, dipped pancakes in honey and had a good laugh. Fatima was not put off by language barriers and tirelessly explained until I understood or until she couldn't go on because of one of her laughing fits at the hilarity of our conversation. Bilal and Hamza munched their pancakes without a word. Whereas most men in Taliouine dominated their families, Bilal seemed in awe of Fatima. She treated him with a kind of good-natured indulgence, as if he was her third child.

Rachid tried to feed Mina a pancake, but she buried her little head in Fatima's lap.

After that, Bilal and Hamza worked until after sunset. Hamza was holding a candle in each hand for Bilal to be able to see.

Ali the electrician had not been around for days. My tolerance was beginning to wear thin. I had to go down to Taghazout to make photo copies for the prolongation. Maybe I would be able to find out what had happened to him.

Before midday, I arrived in the town hall with eighty sheets of paper, four sets of twenty. Each page had to be certified. I was starting to loathe French bureaucracy. Again, I sprinted bravely several times across the main road to buy the required stamps, narrowly avoiding a collision with a van, lopsided, due to the amount of sheep on the roof rack. After the usual ceremony of sticking, stamping and signing, I was sent to the police station to hand in two sets of the application. The rest remained in the village hall.

Of course, it was not going to work straight away.

"You bring more stamps, sixty dirham, and paper of residence," the sturdy police officer barked and turned his back on me.

I did not have a paper of residence nor had I ever heard of it before.

"*Monsieur*, I don't have a paper of residence."

The officer leant over.

"You pay more stamps, twenty dirham, I write paper for you, *insha'allah*," he suggested with a grin, securing a nice little *baksheesh* for himself.

I saw my friend Yassin shortly, but I was so wound up about the electrician not showing up, that soon after my arrival in the café it stood between us.

"Maybe he has another job," Yassin defended Ali.

I left, feeling abandoned by my friend, by the electrician, by everybody.

When I returned to Taliouine Larbi had delivered sand from the beach. To use sand from the beach for building work was not allowed due to its high salt content, but it was much cheaper. I did not see any harm in using it for plastering the inside walls.

I knew from the past, when I spent my nights on the beach, that getting the sand is a cloak-and-dagger-operation, carried out in the dark of moonless nights. I was surprised that there was still sand left on the beach after years of carting it away to the numerous building sites.

Hamza and I shovelled the sand into the house. Bilal plastered all four walls of the bedroom. We were working well; there were no problems. And yet, I could feel something dark looming. In my experience, as soon as everything seemed fine, bad news were just around the corner. I steeled myself.

"Mina," Bilal said suddenly and pointed at the concrete staircase.

"Mina what?"

Bilal's hands and feet made a motion as if tumbling down the stairs. He grinned sheepishly.

My God. A girl so fragile that it could be blown away by a mouse's sneeze had fallen down fourteen concrete steps. My concrete steps. On my building site. My responsibility. I held my breath.

"Mina, *ca va bien*," Hamza offered with a friendly smile. Bilal nodded.

"Why was Mina here?" I did not understand.

Bilal and Hamza were outdoing each other stammering a plausible explanation. All I could understand was that Fatima had to go somewhere, so Bilal had to look after Mina.

Mina was now with Melikha. I raced across to find the little girl sitting on the floor playing happily with baby Mohamed.

"Mina *ifulki*." Melikha said.

This time I had been lucky.

I made Bilal understand that under no circumstances were children allowed on the site. He nodded several times, the sheepish grin wiped off his face.

Chapter Twenty Five

The electrician arrived at nine o'clock. I was stupidly grateful and decided not to ask about his absence in the past days.

Ali rummaged through the box and held out the remains of the cable.

"*Madame – fini*," he said.

It seemed impossible to me that he should run out of cable so soon. He had only done a handful of day's work on my house so far. Perhaps he had miscalculated what he needed.

As Bilal and Hamza were taking a holiday, I decided to drive to Agadir to buy the stamp for the police officer and the cable for the electrician. I left Ali some cheese and bread for lunch and set off.

I missed my friend Yassin and stopped in Taghazout for a chat and a mint tea with him, like in old times.

"I am happy to see you." His blue eyes held mine for a while. Then he bent his head over the bread and honey we were sharing.

I said nothing. Yassin was not the kind of man who talked about feelings and was probably embarrassed at what had slipped out. My eyes wandered across the street where I spotted Ali the electrician hanging out with some men. I dropped my bread into the dish. I grabbed Yassin's arm and asked him to tell Ali to come over. Ali came reluctantly.

I was furious. "Why are you not working?"

Ali spoke, Yassin translated: "He finished because tomorrow is *Aid el Kebir*."

I had reached boiling point. The way Ali only turned up now and then, the little bits of work he did when he came. He was holding up the work progress, as Bilal could only plaster the walls after the electrician had finished the wiring. I had enough.

"You will finish the work by Thursday or I will not pay you," I said, jabbing my finger in his direction.

Ali spoke again, and Yassin translated. "He asks you for more money, for the fete."

I left to go for a walk or I would have exploded on the terrace of Yassin's cafe. I had already given Ali half his wages in advance. I felt exploited. I had even left lunch for him.

When I returned to the cafe, Yassin said to me, "You should give him money. Tomorrow is *Aid el Kebir*. He must buy sheep."

"Yassin," I said, "Ali could have come every day and done his job. He could have finished the whole house by today and got all the money I owe him. But he did not come. If he has another job to do – ok. I could understand it. But I saw him hanging around with nothing to do. And even then he would not come to work."

I did not know why Yassin was so much on Ali's side. I had seen him fire his employees because they did not sweep the floor properly. He was a slave driver when it came to his labourers. Maybe Ali had not paid him his commission yet.

When I arrived at the police station, a different shift was working. This time I heard that a residence paper was not necessary, but the officer still refused to take my papers.

"*Après la fete, insha'allah.*"

I wondered if I would ever be able to persuade somebody to take my forms.

It seemed that with *Aid el Kebir* nearing life in Morocco was grinding to a halt.

On my return to Taliouine, I saw a black four-wheel drive with French number plates parked in front of Cherifa's house, like a mirage in the desert. It blocked the whole pathway. The legendary Philippe must have returned from France and was visiting the future in-laws. Animated chatter, excited shrieks and the desperate bleating of a sheep-that-knows drifted across from the house. The sheep must have been a present from Philippe.

I hung about in front of my house, examining the plaster lengthily and hoping to catch a glimpse of Philippe when he climbed into his great big car. Small dull men always have big cars to make up for their shortness, especially the ones who suffer from hair loss.

I did not have to wait long. Soon a man appeared in the doorway, trying to make his way to his car through the throng of women who were surrounding him like group of excited teenagers. He was neither small nor bald. On the contrary, he was tall and tanned, with a mop of blond hair. He seemed familiar. He looked at me and stopped in his track. I looked at him and felt my heart drop onto the stony ground.

Nice looking bloke, I thought in a mixture of delight and horror, trying to pick up my heart from the floor and put it back in its place. Why do I never meet them? Or better, why do I always meet them AFTER they had coupled up with another woman? And who was the woman in the souk? And why had she called him "Luc"? And why had he responded when his name was obviously Philippe? What game was he playing? And why was I having this inane crush on him, when he was going to get married to my adorable neighbour Nadah? I did not have a single answer at hand.

Philippe was Not Nick. Handsome man with no shirt on in Agadir's one and only laundrette. His eyes were fixed on mine; probably trying to remember where he had seen me before. Helplessly I stared back at him, wishing he was not so much of a "fiancé".

The future in-laws were flustering around him like hens around a cockerel and did not realise what was going on. Philippe broke into a smile, a lovely smile, not at all embarrassed, as it would be more appropriate in this situation.

"*Bonjour*," he called.

"Hello," I said politely.

Cherifa sensed forbidden vibrations in the air and shielded the precious prey from me. The cluster of women pushed Philippe towards and then into his car. His eyes were clinging laughingly on to mine, and with a shrug of the shoulders, he let himself be shoved into his car.

He sped off, leaving us coughing and spluttering in a cloud of dust. It slightly diminished my enthusiasm for him. But only fractionally.

"*Madame*!" Nadah shouted happily. She came skipping over to me. "*Shuf*!"

She turned a comical little pirouette. Philippe had brought her a mini skirt from France, which she was wearing over her leggings. Exposing so much leg was a daring thing to do, but she was so happy and proud that I did not want to spoil it for her by being conventional.

"Very nice, Nadah," I said and pointed my thumb upwards.

Nadah pulled out a mobile phone and proudly presented it to me.

"Philippe." She said.

Philippe had given her a mobile phone! Why on earth did he do that when they had no language in common? What was going to happen when the batteries ran out? Nashiema approached. She tipped the side of her forehead and laughed.

That evening I saw Nadah standing on the roof of the house in true soap-opera-style: a dark silhouette against the setting sun, upright, looking longingly towards the shimmering lights of Agadir and then at the little telephone, which was sleeping quietly and peacefully in her hand.

"Sod that man," I thought angrily.

It was the day of *Aid el Kebir*, and a festive atmosphere had descended onto the village. Dressed in their finest and most colourful robes, my neighbours were waiting for the moment when the throat of their sheep was to be cut. And the sheep, sensing that something awful and final was about to happen, bleated their hearts out. The king would be the first to cut, broadcasted on television, and the rest of Morocco's population followed his example. I did not know how my neighbours knew when to do IT, because nobody had television or radio and the mosque was too far away to be heard. I stayed indoors. I did not want to witness the ritual slaughtering. Suddenly the desperate bleating stopped, and when I popped my head out of the window, I saw a thin red rivulet flowing down the path.

My attempts to hide away failed. My neighbour Yassin visited and invited me to Cherifa's house. I was seated on a cushion on the kitchen floor, where all of Cherifa's daughters had already spread out. Nashiema, Nadah and Yasmina, and even her older daughters Fatna and Mina had arrived from Agadir.

Nashiema tore off some bread and pushed it into my hand. "*Mange, mange!*" She pointed at the *tajine* dish in the middle of the room.

Carefully I dipped my bread into the sizzling clay pot, remembering the desperate bleating only two hours earlier. I had never eaten fresher meat in my life before.

Nashiema placed brochettes with intestines in front of me. I tried to eat as little as possible without appearing impolite. Firstly, because you are not expected to stuff yourself when invited, rather the opposite, and secondly, I did not think my stomach would take kindly to the half-cooked liver. Meanwhile Cherifa was stuffing an empty sheep stomach with bits of minced up something.

The mood was merry and chatty.

"Mohamed." Cherifa cried and waved with her stuffing hand that he had gone away. Blobs of minced up sheep rained down on me.

The women twittered in competition, and I learned that Mohamed had left for Taroudant, for good, and Nashiema and Samir without food and drink. Not only that, he had also had beaten Nashiema up, taken her savings and was conducting an affair with a German tourist. Nashiema smiled her beautiful smile and looked neither battered nor bothered.

"Mangez, Madame!" She pushed another piece of bread in my direction.

Later Cherifa accompanied me into the yard and proudly showed me the furless limp remains of a sheep, hung up in the shadow on a make-shift washing line like an old blanket.

Back in my house, I hardly had time to sit down when there was another knock on the door. It was Moulham, inviting me to his house. How nice of everyone to include me in the family festivities! Moulham's family had prepared a *tajine,* which showed no sign of offal or intestine, but contained meat as soft as butter. I could taste the argan flavour. Sheep from this area of Morocco are highly in demand. They feed on the pungent meaty leaves of the argan tree, which gives the meat a unique herby flavour. It reminded me of Provence, where the meat tastes of thyme and rosemary, because during their life time sheep feast on fresh herbs all day long.

Moulham confirmed the latest gossip about Mohamed and Nashiema.

"Will he come back, you think? Who is going to feed Nashiema and Samir?"

Moulham shrugged his shoulders.

"Family give food."

When I left I found Hamza, Fatima and Melikha loitering on the pathway outside Moulham's house. Hamza had drunk a whole *litro* and was completely wasted. His head was lolling somewhere near Melikha's chest.

"Monsieur! Bonjour, Monsieur!" he called out to me, and the girls shrieked with laughter.

I was happy to see my neighbours in such a merry mood.

I returned to my house and was left in peace to potter around and indulge in fantasies about state-of-the-art interior design and furniture, in case I won the lotto.

The next day Taliouine was as peaceful as I had never seen it before. Everybody seemed to be on visits outside the village. I went for a long walk in solitude up and down the surrounding hills, thinking as usual what type of people lived over the next hills and indulging in the idea of THE HIKE. But before I could set off, I had a house to finish.

I was roaming through the house making a list what had to be done, when my eyes fell on the box with the electrical bits and pieces. As if to find an answer, I rummaged through the parts and found to my surprise that there was not much left. Where had all those things gone? Six hundred metres of cable had disappeared. Switches and sockets had magically reduced in numbers without having been mounted anywhere in the house. Not in my house, anyway.

In the evening Melikha brought me freshly baked bread and I gave her a packet of English biscuits in return.

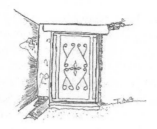

Chapter Twenty-Six

After a sleepless night worrying about the electrician I had an early breakfast. As Bilal and Hamza were still on holiday, I decided to spend a day away from the village and visit my traveller friends on the beach. I was dying for a bit of intelligible conversation, which was not conducted in imperatives, which did not involve hands, feet, and unspeakable Berber words and which had nothing to do with building houses.

I stopped at the police station. Officially the fete was over and there was no excuse not to accept my application. I received a provisional prolongation until my permit to stay was granted. If my application was rejected I would have to leave the country within twenty-four hours and try to re-enter from Spain.

Afterwards, I drove into Agadir to replace the missing bits and pieces in the electrician's box.

"*Combien*?" The two men in the shop laughed hysterically, when I told them that Ali had used up six hundred metres of cable and asked for more. "Enough for a whole village!"

"Only hand out material necessary for the next step," one of the men advised me, "otherwise you give for him to take."

"*Merci, Monsieur*."

To my surprise I soon pulled up at the European style supermarket Marjane, driven by a craving for comfort food from home like chocolate digestives, Jaffa cakes and English tea. I realised that the experience with the electrician disturbed me more than I had thought. I felt the whole project was starting to take its toll. I was down to my last reserves and in danger of falling back into my down-at-the-bottom-diet, which usually consisted exclusively of biscuits, tea and bananas. Any thought of cooked food would make me feel sick.

I also bought some food for Samir and Nashiema. Laden with fruit, yoghurt, nuts and biscuits for Samir, chocolates for Nashiema, biscuits, tea, and bananas for me I left the supermarket in high spirits. I had also bought a bottle of wine for a night on the beach.

I bounced across the fields to the beach, parked between other campers and vans and enjoyed the ocean outside my window. I was still capable of conversing in complete sentences. I had a few glasses of wine, a good laugh and managed to forget about the electrician. I spent the night on the beach. It was a special treat. It was a feeling of freedom after the claustrophobic surroundings up in the village. I heard waves and seagulls and slept peacefully, until a voice woke me up just after sunrise:

"*Madame*, *baguette*? Bread? *Brot*?"

My head was pounding.

The holiday of *Aid el Kebir* was finally over, even in Taliouine, and Bilal and Hamza returned to work.

When I arrived with my van the next day, I found Hamza busily carrying sand and mixing cement. Bilal and I had agreed that I would place the keys for the door under a stone by the side of the house, so he could start work early in the morning without having to wake me up should I still be asleep. Or in case I spent the night on the beach.

"*Bonjour*, *Madame*," Hamza shouted happily and waved at me.

It seemed to be heading for a perfect day especially with the electrician walking up the track towards my house. A vision of me moving into a fully wired and plastered house very soon made my day.

"*Bonjour*," I greeted Ali pleasantly.

Ali was not alone. He had brought a friend to translate that he, Ali, was going to come and finish the work the following day. *Insha'allah*. With that they left again. I rubbed my eyes. Maybe it had been a mirage, being so close to the desert.

Ali did come back the next day, together with his brother. When I tried to challenge him about the stolen bits, he blamed it on Bilal.

Then Ali and his brother set to work.

In the end he used seven fuses, just as much as I had left after the theft. Why did he make me buy twelve? It dawned on me that he had planned to take five for himself from the beginning. The same applied for the other bits and pieces, including the six hundred metres of cable. I realised now why he took me all the way to Inezgane, leading me through a maze to a tiny shop, which he hoped I would never find again.

Things started to get worse. The electrician fixed switches in the wrong places and blamed it on me, saying I had changed the plan. Nevertheless, the two men worked fast. When it came to testing the wiring, they regretfully shook their head. The battery of their meter had run out.

I insisted on using one of the batteries from the van. As soon as it turned out that many sockets did not work I stopped. I was worried about my battery getting destroyed.

"Go home, and come back tomorrow with proper equipment." I shouted.

Swearing and shouting, the two brothers left for Taghazout.

The incident had shaken me. I sat down on a boulder on the edge of the *farine* to calm down.

I suspected that it was not an accident that his meter was not working. Ali had done a bad job and thought I would just dish out the money when he declared the work done, thinking a woman would not dare challenge him.

My neighbour Yassin crouched next to me: "Ali – *khaib. Voleur*. No good."

193

A thief! Yassin looked worried for a moment then his usual laissez-faire expression returned and a lazy smile spread over his face.

"Madame – *travail, s'il-vous-plait*?" he asked, handling fondly a cigarette he was about to devour.

I hesitated for a moment, thinking of the unpleasant affair about the parking. I had not seen much of Yassin in the recent weeks, because he was involved in his own building project. He believed that the ancient part of Cherifa's cluster, which he and his little family inhabited, could be sold to a wealthy tourist for a nice lump of dirham. In case one of those people happened to come along, Yassin wanted to be prepared. He had started building a lean-to type dwelling adjoining Cherifa's house. I had never before seen Yassin work so hard.

He was my neighbour, a loyal one and he deserved another chance. And he and his family needed money.

"Okay, Yassin, *azih*!"

He followed me into the house, where I explained to him what I needed: brick walls for the kitchen surfaces. Yassin nodded eagerly. We agreed a price and he went to work straight away.

Although I remained apprehensive as to what Yassin would do to my kitchen walls, I started wondering if I should not have asked him in the first place to build my house. The little one-room house he was building had so much more character than mine with its uneven walls, undulating plaster and wooden roof.

By the end of the day Yassin had built walls so lopsided that any work surface fitted on top of it would resemble the ocean below on a stormy day.

"Take it down, Yassin, and build it again tomorrow," I sign-languaged.

Yassin nodded and left for his dwelling, his cheerful whistling cutting through the silence of the darkening evening. Another day of paid work had miraculously materialised.

The electrician arrived with his brother, but not with a working meter. The two men were hanging around outside the house.

"What are you waiting for?" I asked finally, with my neighbour Yassin's help.

Ali was waiting for his money.

"You show me that everything works and I will pay you."

Ali said he would go to the police. Fine, I hoped he would. Maybe I should go to the police myself.

I snatched his meter, which was lying on the floor. I switched it on. It worked perfectly.

"So why are you not using it?" I said holding it under his nose. "Is it because you know already that nothing is working? Do you think I am a stupid woman and will pay you anyway?"

The electrician's face coloured with anger.

"*Attendez*! Wait here!" I said.

I drove down to Taghazout and, as usual, came quickly across somebody who could help me: Amir, an electrician, who worked for Yassin-the-builder. Readily, for a few dirham, he accompanied me to Taliouine. Ali could hardly restrain himself when Amir looked at the installation.

It was pathetic. Nothing worked. The terrace lamp was not even connected.

With Amir's help, I told Ali that I would get another electrician to check and redo the wiring.

With a murderous glance and swearing under his breath, Ali stomped off down the hill. His brother followed him quickly.

Agitated, I returned my attention to Bilal only to find him struggling to finish his work on the top floor. As usual, Hamza spent his day leaning on the shovel shouting "*oho*" and Yassin – well, Yassin was Yassin!

I sighed. Things were not going too well at the moment, to be positive, and my patience had become virtually non-existent. I took refuge in my van and listened to Taliouine. I did not feel romantic about it or homely, just exhausted. The women were always shouting, the children were always screaming. The high-pitched noise level was getting to my nerves. Yasmina's clucking just outside my van was sending me up the walls.

"Ah – ah – ah – ah – ah!"

This meant as much as "here are some scraps for you, cats and dogs!"

It was like a madhouse.

There was an endless shouting of names forwards and backwards across the village. Nobody bothered to go round and knock on the door when they could shout across for the person they wished to talk to.

"Yasmina! Yasminaaaaa! Yaaaasminaaaa!"

Help!

In amongst the village noises I heard the trotting of sandaled feet, of many sandaled feet.

"It is lovely up here."

"Look at the view."

"I wish I had a house here. Cannot find that view in Manchester."

There was a knock at the door of my van. Outside stood Lahcen from Ait Tabbia, with yet another group of English tourists trailing through the mountains to have a nosey look at the Berber people and their houses.

"Can they have a look inside your house?" Lahcen asked, nodding in the direction of his herd.

I led the whole group under excited chatter up the steps until they reached the top terrace.

"It is so beautiful here."

"You are very lucky."

They were stunned and envious, and I smiled weakly at their impression of a paradise. Looking down over the walls, I noticed that the small yard in front of Cherifa's door had been freshly concreted. Probably with my *cimar*, which was kindly provided by Allah, when I was not looking. I smiled dryly.

Maybe I should start serving cream teas on the terrace.

After sunset, I fled Taliouine and escaped to the beach.

I had not seen my friend Yassin for a while and visited him in his café the next morning. He invited me to share breakfast with him. I loved the early mornings in Taghazout. The air was still cool, but a hot spring day lay ahead. Taghazout was waking up. The stalls were being prepared, goods and fresh bread being delivered.

As usual, we had milky instant coffee and oven-warm bread, which we dipped in a bowl of honey.

"You are not happy," my friend observed.

"No, I am not." I told him about the unpleasant development concerning the electrician. The electrician he had recommended.

When I had finished, Yassin shook his head in sympathy. He accompanied me to Taliouine to see for himself.

He moved through the house, knocking here and there, examining the odd cable and tutting empathetically. Maybe he finally felt guilty because he had introduced me to Ali.

Life in Taliouine carried on. Bilal plastered his way through the house. Hamza continued to mix the odd load of cement from time to time and to rest between those jobs, talking his unintelligible speak and watching others work. The plaster was a patchwork of different shades of grey because Hamza was still not able to mix equal amounts every time. I had given up. Anyway, did it matter if the plaster was uneven? It definitely was one of less important things in life.

Only Bilal could really understand what Hamza was saying and had taken to the same slurry way of speaking. Sometimes it felt like coming into a nursery, where I would walk in and shout: "Morning! Everybody happy?" The two brothers would chuckle delightedly and utter some strange noises, maybe along the line: "What an old bitch!"

Yassin had worked hard on the support walls for the kitchen work surface and they were acceptably straight.

"*Madame?*"

"*Mezyan, Yassin.*"

He smiled.

Chapter Twenty-Seven

A grey rainy day brought a colourful encounter with Ali. I was unsettled by the amount of rain I had seen here so far, although I was told it only happened every ten years.

Ali arrived in a battered car, accompanied by four men with no-nonsense expressions for intimidating purposes. They had brought with them a car battery. I did not allow them to carry out any testing in case the battery blew up. I did not trust this clan anymore.

I repeated, that I would instruct a genuine electrician to check the wiring.

Ali pointed angrily at the genuine electrician he had brought up, who glared at me under knitted eyebrows and looked like the Moroccan equivalent to Al Capone's right hand. I turned and went back into the house.

Ali collected his tools and his ladder, hissing and muttering, and the whole group left.

Nadah strolled past cradling her silent mobile phone like a favourite pet. Even if it never rang, she was proud to possess this piece of western wealth, which everyone here was craving for. Anyway, Philippe would not phone her unless she understood what he said.

"Nadah, you must learn French." I stepped out of my house.

She giggled and slipped her arm through mine. I felt tiny next to her.

"*Oho*," she said.

"No? Come on, I will teach you. You – teach – me – Berber – and – I – teach – you – French," I explained with hands and feet.

But Nadah did not want to learn French. Instead, she indicated me to take my shoes off. With a sigh, I gave in. As always. We swapped shoes and paraded through the village. The children followed us, laughing, singing and forever shouting *Madame*, while Nadah's arm was hooked protectively through mine.

When we returned, the four-wheeler was once again parked in front of Cherifa's house.

Since the last meeting I had not seen Philippe again, let alone spoken to him. I had so far managed to escape another encounter. I had to get this crush out of my head. It was obviously not going anywhere. He was engaged to Nadah, and all we shared were a couple of comical encounters – hardly enough to base a romantic daydream on. I liked Nadah too much to destroy her chance of a better life.

"*Beslama*, Nadah, your fiancé has arrived."

"Bye, bye, *Madame*."

No one could say Nadah had no talent for languages.

I felt sad, when I entered my house. Lonely. Nadah, Nashiema and Melikha were the only ones who were prepared to take me on unfalteringly, treating me with the protective care of someone looking after a wounded animal. I should be grateful for their affection and not mope about the rest of the village. Who knows, in time I might make more friends.

A gentle knock on the door woke me from my sombre musings. The village people are not known for knocking gently. For a split second, I felt I should not answer the door but hideaway in the darkest corner of my house. Instead, I flew to the door and pulled it open.

"Hi," Philippe said. "Everybody is talking about your house. It even seems to have become part of our *randonnes* as far

200

as I have heard. *Experience Authentic Berber Life,*" he quoted laughingly from what must have been an advertisement for his company. "Would you let me have a look at your house?" he asked.

"Yes, of course, no problem. Come in. Of course I don't mind," I babbled away, wishing I could do hundreds of things at the same time like hide the greasy spot on my t-shirt from the last *tajine*, fluff up my hair, put make up on and my pink dress, and, and, and….

He stepped past me. I watched him look round and take in every detail.

"You have done well," he said. "It is not an easy project. I guess you encounter many difficulties."

A decent bloke indeed, I thought, trying to withstand the urge to throw myself into his arms and have a good cry.

"Not too bad. I'll manage." I croaked.

He looked at me. "Let me know if you need any help. I'll be around for a while."

I followed him up the steps. Nice bum, I thought - out of bounds, though. I came quickly to the point, which interested me most.

"When are you and Nadah going to get married?" I asked him.

We were standing side by side on the top terrace. The nearness of his body radiated through mine like warm sunshine.

Philippe shrugged his shoulders.

"Cherifa's wishful thinking," was his vague answer in a tone, which indicated that he wished no further discussion of the subject. His glance lingered somewhere on the horizon like Nadah's did evening after evening, when she was listening to the silence of her phone.

I wondered if he was just stringing her along. Why would he do that? The world of Taliouine was full of mysteries.

"I like your house," Philippe said. He plucked his eyes off the horizon, settled them on mine and smiled.

I felt my face burning. I needed to speak to lighten up the situation and hide my feelings.

"It is not my original plan. I wanted to build a traditional Berber house with a courtyard and doors leading off into rooms. And a terrace on the top for the view. But when I heard that you were going to add a second floor to Cherifa's house I had to go higher otherwise I would have been staring against your wall. And here we are. Higher than anybody else." I attempted a hearty laugh, but it was more a squeak.

"I was going to do what?" he asked, furrowing his brows.

"Well, everybody told me that when you and Nadah are getting married you will build rooms upstairs and live there with her," I explained.

Philippe laughed out loudly. It was a pleasant laugh. Not a roaring one, not too loud and not too hysterical. It was warm and friendly.

"I have known Cherifa for many years. She is a master of leading other people's lives and creating rumours."

He became serious.

"Watch out for her."

"I have been warned before," I told him, "by my friend Yassin."

Leaning on my balustrade, we stared down into Cherifa's cluster, watching her darting in and out of her kitchen.

"Your name is Philippe?" I asked finally.

"Yes… of course!"

"And the woman in the souk? She called you Luc, didn't she? Do you come with a supply of different names for different women?"

Philippe laughed.

"Luc is my second name. Florence prefers it to Philippe. Florence is my sister."

Lahcen's girlfriend, I remembered.

"I must go now," Philippe said.

We made our way down the staircases. He stepped through the door and turned round.

"It was nice talking to you," he smiled.

"Nice talking to you, too," I answered.

202

"My name is Kate," I shouted after him. "Not *Madame*. Should anyone tell you my name is *Madame* – it is wrong. It is Kate!"

He turned round. "I know."

How did he know?

Seconds later his car disappeared down the hill, and not a speck of dust was stirred up. I laughed.

The cistern needed cleaning. I had been postponing the job, but now, with the new pump and a delivery of fresh water needed it was best to get rid of all the rubbish and dirt deep down on the bottom and start afresh. I had a strong aversion to lowering myself into a hole with a diameter of one metre, not because of the muck but its resemblance to an Agatha-Christie-setting: "Twenty years later John dug up what looked like a cistern and found the body of a middle-aged woman. It was clear that she had desperately fought to find a way out after somebody must have locked the lid."

Luckily, my neighbour Yassin volunteered to clean the cistern one evening, for a bit of extra money.

Bilal also stayed late, long after dark, and plastered the bathroom, because just before sunset Hamza had mixed an enormous amount of cement and it needed to be used up. Bilal would not let it go to waste. The two of them worked by candlelight, while Yassin rummaged in the depth of the cistern. I sat on the floor and found it a rather cosy atmosphere.

Yassin with his usual short-lived enthusiasm for work soon declared the cistern clean and left. He had fished out bits of old bucket and the odd stone, but not done any cleaning, which was so important for me.

Bilal was embarrassed by this and shook his head. After his candlelight plastering session, he insisted on going into the cistern himself and cleaning it properly. Although heavy rainfall made it easier for him, he was up until the early hours of the morning. I was immeasurably grateful and watched all night over the lock of the cistern lid.

Wandering around the house the next morning my bleary eyes fell upon the shelf in the bedroom wardrobe, which my neighbour Yassin had built the previous day. The shelf was bending in the middle as if an invisible elephant was sitting on it. I sacked Yassin.

He did not mind at all and whisked Mina off to the souk in Aourir. They were giggling like two excited children. When they came back, both of them were wearing ridiculously unsuitable shoes for the mountains – hers were high-heeled, his were as white as snow – but they were proud of their extravagant purchases, and a breeze of carefreeness was for once floating through the stuffy pathways of Taliouine.

Their happiness infected me, and soon I was smiling and humming.

But it was not going to last.

DOWN TOWARDS THE SEA

Chapter Twenty-Eight

I don't know why, amidst all the merriment, I suddenly
remembered my precious cut-out unit. I had been meaning to
find a safe place, especially for the guarantee card, which
seemed even more important. I left the assortment of villagers
who had gathered around Mina and Yassin and ran into my
house. I pulled out the box of electrical bits – the cut-out unit
was still there. The guarantee card though was missing.

After turning my house upside down, I had to face the fact
that someone might have taken it.

"Where is Najib?" I shouted at the bleak grey walls.
"Najib?"

My neighbour Yassin had followed me and was leaning
against the door frame, juggling small stones with one hand,
while fingering the habitual cigarette with the other.

"Yes. Najib."

"Najib *l'électricien*?"

"Yes, Yassin, Najib the electrician. Do you know anything
about him?" I turned my palms upwards and looked at him
questioningly.

Yassin chucked the stones over his shoulder onto the path
and wiped his hand on his dark trousers, leaving white chalky
trails.

205

"Najib, *il habite a Tamraght.*"

"He lives in Tamraght? Do you mean the small village three kilometres away from here? Are you sure?" I clasped my hands together and turned round. "Yassin my friend, what can I do for you, do you want to build another shelf? Do you need cement – *cimar* – for your house, or a tool or sand – *sable*? Help yourself." I danced around my building site, pointing at various piles. "What would I do without you, Yassin?"

Yassin only laughed, tipped the side of his head as if I had gone mad, enjoyed a puff of his cigarette and walked off.

I manoeuvred my van out of its parking space and slithered down the track. After last night's heavy rain, the surface of the track was as soft as dough.

Once again, I found myself in the builders' merchant in Tamraght. Ahmed was sorting through a box of screws.

"*Bonjour*, Ahmed."

Ahmed looked up and adjusted his *Kufi* cap.

"Ah, *bonjour, Madame, ca va*?" he greeted me and shook my hand. "How is the building site? I heard you are making progress."

"Yes, I am. But without your help it wouldn't have been possible."

Ahmed waved his hand dismissingly.

"What can I do for you today?"

"Do you know Najib, the electrician?"

Although I called Tamraght a village, it was a rather large development, more like a small town and I should be very lucky if Najib was known to Ahmed.

"Najib, *l'électricien*?" Ahmed said and lifted the receiver off the telephone. "*Mais oui*, do you want to speak to him?"

"Yes, please – no wait, I would like to meet him."

After the usual Berber staccato exchange, Ahmed hung up.

"Najib is busy. He will come to your house tomorrow at ten. Now, do you, need anything, maybe some of these beautiful shiny screws, or a pretty little tool?"

I laughed. "You will never stop making fun of me, will you?"

206

Ahmed dropped a selection of screws and nails into a brown paper bag and handed it over to me.

"*Un cadeau*," he said. "A woman building can never have enough of those."

Just as I drove off, I saw Ali the electrician arriving with a new client, a European looking client, to buy bits and bobs for the new job. I was astonished. Ali had taken me all the way to Inezgane to be able to cheat on me. Why not him? Because I was a woman?

It had started to rain again. I spun and skidded up to Taliouine and sat trapped in my *parking*. The rain did not stop all day. I could not believe the amount of rain pouring down onto this part of Morocco, which claims to have 365 days of sunshine a year. What was I doing here?

Najib arrived at ten o'clock the next morning and ten minutes later, I had spilled out the whole unfortunate episode with Ali.

Najib shook his head.

"I am sorry about it," he said, and yet, he neither commented on it nor did he express disapproval of Ali's behaviour.

He set to work and checked the wiring.

"It does not seem too bad, but I can't tell for sure," he finally said. "I suggest you hire a generator in Aourir. Then I will come back and together with your electrician I will measure the installation."

We agreed the day after tomorrow for the tests.

"The guarantee card of my cut-out unit has disappeared."

He looked up.

"You cannot connect to the main supply without it. It is illegal."

"No chance?"

"No chance. Where did you keep the card, in this box?"

"Yes," I murmured.

"A mistake."

I was learning slowly, that in Morocco thieves are not the only ones held responsible for theft, but also the victims, for failing to lock away their possessions.

After Najib had gone, I drove to Inezgane and made my way through the maze of the builders' souk. When I finally found the shop, where Ali had bought the bits, the shopkeeper was unable to hand out another guarantee card.

"Every unit has its own card," the shopkeeper explained. "You must phone the company in Casablanca and explain your dilemma. Maybe you will find help."

He tore a piece of cardboard off a box and wrote down a telephone number for me.

Making phone calls has always been something I avoided if possible, even if it was in my own language. Having to phone a company in Casablanca where people spoke French, Berber or even Arabic, from a moody and uncooperative public phone, made me giggle hysterically.

"Can you phone for me, please?" I begged the shopkeeper.

But he had already turned his back on me.

"No, you have to speak to them."

In the end, it was easier than anticipated. A kind sounding woman answered the phone and listened patiently to my almost unintelligible stutter in French. I felt my face getting red and hot. All that had to be done was for Najib to send a fax when connecting my house to the electricity. The woman helpfully repeated the fax number several times until my shaking hand had noted it down correctly.

"*Merci pour votre patience.*" I wondered if the French and English were using the same word.

"*Je suis en pris.*" She hung up.

I left the phone booth. My self-esteem had increased a few notches and I started humming. Self-confident, I retreated to one of the cafes for lunch, ignoring the stares of the all male clientele. I had two portions of calamar, fried in a pan made from concrete, which merged into the work surface of the same material, and wondered why life was made of a chain of challenges.

Two days later, I collected a generator from a garage in Aourir. It took two men to lift it through the back door into my van. When I arrived at my house, Najib and Ali were already there. My neighbour Yassin had joined them.

The following four hours Najib spent trying to make things work, rewiring and changing sockets. Ali did nothing to help. His face was twisted into an arrogant expression, while he was quietly working himself into a rage. Dressed carefully in a neat green overall with child-sized blue Wellington boots and a matching scarf slung rakishly around his neck, he arranged himself on a pile of breeze blocks. He chewed gum with such vehemence, that I could see every muscle in his gaunt face working. I had not realised before how much in love he was with his own appearance, how obsessed with his looks. I remembered ridiculously clean feet in sandals. He was not the type of man who got his hands or feet dirty when working.

Unexpectedly, Ali leapt up, swore and spat at me, then attempted to stab me with his screwdriver. With a cry, I jumped, feeling the draft of the lethal tool on the side of my face. Yassin and Najib were there immediately, winding the screwdriver out of the electrician's hand, shouting at him and pushing him back onto the breezeblocks. He was shaking all over.

I was shivering, hoping the nightmare would end soon. But there was more to come.

Finally, Najib started packing away his tools. "Everything is working now," he said. "It was worse than I thought."

Except for attacking me, Ali had not moved a finger. He probably did not know any more about electrical installations than I did.

Yassin and Najib loaded the generator back into the van. I had to go to Agadir to withdraw money and offered Najib a lift.

When we crawled into the cabin, Ali started shouting. He rolled small boulders in front of my van to stop us from driving off. He hit the bonnet several times with his fist and demanded the rest of the money there and then.

I should not have to pay him any money at all, I thought. At least, I should deduct Najib's fees from the amount. I never suggested anything like that, though. However, I had to go to the bank first, but Ali seemed determined to stop us from leaving the village.

Najib wound his window down and explained.

He did not get through to Ali, who was raging in front of the van. His eyes were flashing madly. The colour of his face signalled danger. He was shaking with fury. He was not going to let me go to a bank. He wanted his money now. And once again, he bombarded the bonnet with his pathetically small fists. He enjoyed the attention of the entire village population who had naturally gathered when the drama began to unfold and who were now watching greedily. Najib tried to calm Ali, but to no avail. Ali was too far gone to be reasonable. We sat for a long time, not knowing what to do.

Najib's fingers started drumming on the dashboard. He was a busy man, with an appointment in Agadir, and probably regretted by now that he had come up to help me, only to be trapped in a forgotten mountain village by a lunatic.

With both hands Ali picked up a rock, lifted it over his head, ready to hurl it through my windscreen. My van was my home. I would not be safe without a windscreen and it would not be easy to get a new one. A whole chain of fresh problems clattered through my head. Clutching a can of pepper spray, I left the van and went over to my neighbour Yassin.

"Yassin, I need two hundred dirham, *deux cent* dirham," I said, hoping my neighbours liked me enough to donate a few dirham each, if they had any. It could help me out of this misery.

To my surprise and without hesitation, Yassin pulled his wallet out of his trouser pocket and took out two one hundred dirham notes – his latest pay.

"*Shokran*, Yassin, my friend." In the future, I would allow him build as many crooked shelves as he wanted.

I quickly climbed back into the cabin. I now had one thousand dirham, which was exactly the amount I owed Ali for the work he had not done. Reluctantly I gave them to Najib, who handed them through the window to Ali. I was annoyed about my own weakness, letting myself be bullied into handing over money to someone who did not deserve it. But I had no idea what else to do. None of the men went near him, either. I felt I was buying my life and peace for the village for one thousand dirham.

Being given the money fuelled Ali's hatred even more. He had thrown the rock down in front of the car and was hitting the bonnet again, demanding five hundred dirham more for *derangement*. I refused. Compensation! Ridiculous! I could not care less if he stayed there forever banging my car with his fists. I would not give him one dirham more.

My neighbour Yassin finally had enough. He was a placid and patient man, but when his limits were reached, it was better not to be on the receiving end. Without major effort, he pulled the flyweight of an electrician away from my car, turned him round and shoved him hard down the piste towards Taghazout, hailing harsh words after him and thus made him stumble off as fast as he could.

When he was a safe distance, Ali turned round to me and made furious I-will-cut-your-throat-gestures. Then he ran down the hill.

"*Shokran, encore*, Yassin," I said gratefully, wondering why no one else had dared to shove the small man down the village path.

Yassin's lazy hedonistic smile had returned to his face, his pace had already slowed down, and the rest of the day he was most likely going to spend on the roof of his mother's house from where he would count the waves, the fishing boats and his blessings.

Silently, Najib and I set off down towards the coast. Ali was waiting behind the next bend, hidden from Yassin and the village people, and made us stop the car by jumping right in front of it. I felt for the can of pepper spray in my lap. Ali had a long aggressive conversation with Najib, during which he demanded five hundred dirham more, while Najib repeated that he would not get them. It was like running in circles. I was getting bored of it and rolled slowly down the track.

"He wants a lift to Taghazout – and *safi*." Najib said.

Alright, if that was a peace offer, I would give him a lift. Ali got out at the top of the village, hardly a distance from where he had stopped us. I did not understand it at all.

I drove Najib to Agadir and paid him for his work. Then I returned the generator to Aourir. I did not go anywhere near Taghazout or Taliouine that evening. I was scared by Ali's threat and took refuge on the campsite outside the fishing village. Abdullah, my friend Yassin's brother, who worked on the campsite, when he was resting between building jobs, was pleased to see me again, but wondered why I was there and not in Taliouine. I gave him a short summary of what had happened.

Abdullah shook his head. "You stay in Camping. No pay nussink – no speak. Welcome."

Then he rushed back into the small hut, made from bamboo and plastic sheets, to boil water for mint tea.

Chapter Twenty-Nine

The next morning I drove back to Taliouine to return Yassin's money. The village people congregated to declare their solidarity. For once, the two estranged families were united, condemning what had happened the day before. Cherifa and Yassin urged me to go to the police and report the electrician. They offered to come with me as witnesses, and Moulham followed their example. I was touched.

I spent the day in fear. I had visions of the electrician coming up the hill, accompanied by his four fearsome looking friends, ready to cut my throat. Or mow down the village in true Al-Capone-style. Bilal and Hamza worked their usual speed, one slowly and the other sporadically, while I was jumping about like a nervous rabbit. For the night, I returned to the safety of the camping site. After he had not shown up during the day, I feared Ali might murder me in the night, in the seclusion of the unlit mountain village.

I started to see some benefit in electricity and streetlights.

On the way to the campsite, I stopped at Yassin's café and told him about the drama in the mountains.

"Tell me his name, please, Yassin. The villagers want me to go to the police."

"I don't know, but I find out," Yassin promised, engrossed in watching a group of people descend from a bus.

213

"Yassin, I am sure you know his name. Everybody knows everything here. And Ali has worked for your family before," I said.

Yassin did not answer. He did not want to get involved. Maybe he was even frightened. Yassin-the-builder was intimidating him, so why not a lunatic like Ali? My eyes fell on two packed travel bags next to the counter.

"Are those yours, Yassin? I did not know you were going away."

He never travelled anywhere except during Ramadan, when his café was shut.

Yassin blushed and avoided my eyes. He was obviously ready to jump onto the bus to Casablanca and hide away until that troublesome woman from England had left for Spain.

"Have a good trip, my friend!" I left the café.

"Kate – wait."

But I did not.

I could not afford staying away from my building site, because as learnt in the past, no work would be done. Low-spirited and apprehensive, I arrived in Taliouine early in the morning and found Bilal and Hamza already at work.

Bilal was working fast and furiously. He covered the bedroom ceiling with his trademark higgledy-piggledy coat of plaster. Handmade, imperfect – full of character. My house might look non-descript on the outside, but inside it was a piece of art.

After sunset, I fled down to Taghazout. I did not know what to do with myself, where to go, who to speak to. I parked by the side of the road to buy bottled water. I could not even visit Yassin in his café and try to make up, because he had gone on this mysterious journey.

But he had not. I met him on a pathway leading down to the beach. To my surprise, he was drunk and pathetically tearful.

"I no sleep last night," he cried, his English all over the place. "You so angry and I think we are not friends. Me, I don't travel nowhere."

214

"Times are a bit difficult, Yassin," I tried to comfort him, touched that he seemed to care. "I thought you were not interested in our friendship anymore. You have been strange lately."

"Many, many problems," he said dismissively.

"So why don't you talk to me? I am your friend. Maybe I can help you."

Yassin stared at me. "I wish," he mumbled, swaying slightly.

I shifted uncomfortably under his gaze. He stood close to me, and the warmth of his body touched my skin.

"Have you found out the electrician's full name?" I asked, embarrassed by the sudden desire to feel his arms around me. We were friends. Yassin would probably have a good laugh if he could read my thoughts.

"You don't need the name. I don't think you should to go to the police," Yassin tried to persuade me. "He is gone now, and he will not come back."

It did not take much to crush those fragile beyond-friendship feelings. "Yassin, I dimly remember that there have been several incidents like this in the past which made me think that you are not on my side."

I was exhausted, physically and emotionally, and left him where he was, a sad drunk figure on a litter-strewn pathway.

Yet, I could not deny that there was a new aspect to our relationship.

When I arrived at the police station in Taghazout to ask about the progress concerning my prolongation, I found out that Ali had already been around to complain about me. I decided to mention the electrician's threat, my fear and the suspected theft.

"If you are frightened, you must not go without telephone. When you have problems, phone us and someone will come to help," the officer advised, but I felt as if he was saying I should not be up there. He was not hostile, but he was not too friendly either, rather irritated. They had enough problems keeping the Moroccan population at bay. They did not need the extra burden of having to look after a foreigner, who happened to make a home here instead of Spain or France. And anyway, I did not have a mobile phone.

"And theft?" he continued. "It was authorized theft. By giving him access to the parts you tempted him to steal."

I sighed.

The days went by, and there was no sign of Ali. I started to calm down. I returned to spending the nights on *le parking*, clutching the pepper gas in my sleep.

"Madame – *travail*?"

My neighbour Yassin had run out of money again.

"Of course, my friend, do whatever you like." I put my thumb up at him.

At least, his shelves had character.

Yassin helped Bilal lay the concrete for the floor of the top terrace. Hamza, now having to mix cement for two people, complained about the double workload and sulked. By now, I wished I could get rid of him without causing a break in the still fragile bridge between the villagers and me. Yassin, sensing a problem here, ended up mixing his own cement. I asked Hamza to pump water, which he did, whilst muttering quietly. He was not happy to work for me anymore, and there didn't seem to be anything I could do about it. As soon as I left the house, he left too and set off across the fields.

Bilal plastered his way up the steps to the top terrace. The staircase looked already ancient and worn. The steps were bending in the middle as if generations of people had trotted up and down. I was very pleased. They were the best feature of my house so far. Apart from Yassin's wardrobe shelf.

Hamza did not come back to work again. It was a perfect solution for all of us. He continued to loiter outside the house, smiling and shouting *Oho, Madame*, but now we were friends and I could laugh about it.

Rain started to pour down onto the village again and it turned cold and windy. Everyone was shivering and miserable. The dwellings, made for sun and warmth, were flooded with water. My neighbours' mattresses and blankets spent their days drying on the roof – if there was sunshine, that is. When the rain continued during the day, everyone had to sleep on wet beds. I was worried about my neighbour Yassin's new lean-to. His roof was made from a plastic sheet, weighed down with sand and sticks, to stop it from blowing away. I did not think it would withstand more rain.

"*Madame!*" Cherifa hammered on the door as if trying to break it down. Polite knocking was alien to her forceful personality. "*Madame! Azih!*"

Patience was not her forte, either.

I opened the door to see Cherifa beaming at me, her hand holding onto the sleeve of a man.

"*La bes*, Cherifa, *ca va?*" I said.

But Cherifa had no time for the polite exchange of greetings and well wishing.

"Abdeladigbeer, *Madame.*"

"Pardon?"

Cherifa pulled the man closer and pointed at him.

"Abdeladigbeer, *Madame.*" She shouted, as if I was deaf.

I assumed it was his name, because he stretched out his hand to me.

"*La bes, Madame.*"

I shook his hand. He was taller and stronger built than the average Berber, dressed in a green army type coat. Rain was dripping from the rim of his brown panama hat. His eyes were kind and the expression on his face was that of a person you would turn to in times of trouble. You would pour out your heart to him and he would make cups of tea and tell you that all will be fine.

He reminded me of my father.

"*Frère* Cherifa, *Madame*," she said proudly, as if she had produced this gentle-looking brother herself. "*Travailler?*"

I looked into his eyes and saw a load taken off my shoulders. Here was someone who would be able to handle Yassin and Bilal, who would even have known how to deal with

Ali the electrician. But it was no good if I could not even pronounce his name.

"Abdela. . . . . digby?" I ventured.

"*Moi* - Digby – *c'est bien, Madame*." He bowed slightly.

"*Et moi* - Kate – *c'est bien*, Digby." I smiled.

We shook hands.

Bilal was not well. His plastering became more and more irregular, until even I had to admit it was past being artistic. He moved slowly and looked pained.

"*Ca va*, Bilal?" I was worried, watching his pale strained face struggling to produce a grin.

"*Wacha*, Madame." Tiny bubbles of sweat covered his forehead.

The concrete on the floor of the first terrace and landing was being laid. Digby turned out to be exactly what I had hoped for: experienced, hard working and assertive. Together the three of them worked fast and effectively and I began to relax. Things seemed to be getting better. The building work was going ahead rapidly. My spirits lifted, and I was getting excited about the possibility of being able to finish my house sooner than I had hoped.

Every day, Digby worked from sunrise to sunset, only stopping for the occasional glass of tea and cake, and a dark brown cigarette, which smelt of pine. In the evenings, I had taken to joining him for a cigarette on the *farine*. He smiled, but never talked, just smoked and sipped tea, staring down into the darkening valley. We would sit there together, thinking and smoking. I felt comfortable and safe in his vicinity and enjoyed the tranquillity. After a while, I would get up.

"*Bonne nuit*, Digby."

"*Bonne nuit*, Kate, *bonne nuit*."

He never called me *Madame.*

One step forwards, two steps backwards. Never before had I experienced this as often as here in Taliouine. The hope of being able to move into my house in the near future evaporated when Bilal finally admitted that he was sick. His face was ashen, with dark rings under his eyes. During the day, he had frequently disappeared across the field.

I told him to stay at home and ordered a two-days-holiday. Bilal dropped mortarboard and trowel and staggered off, clutching his stomach.

Gastric flu was spreading rapidly amongst the village people. Watching the endless line of men, women and children moving forwards and backwards across the fields, I decided it was better to disappear to the beach for a while, trying to escape the bug.

Two days later work slowly started again. Bilal only managed to plaster half the bedroom. He obviously had not recovered, but did not want to stay away from work for another day.

From my terrace, I watched Mohamed, Nashiema's husband, walking up the path with plastic bags of food. He dumped them in front of Nashiema's house and disappeared again. This had become an accustomed sight as it happened every two or three days. Unusual though was the fact that a police car came up the piste as soon as Mohamed had disappeared through the back of the village.

A man in a grey uniform emerged from the four-wheeler. It was the officer from Taghazout who had advised me about the electrician.

He knocked on Nashiema's door. She opened, with Samir bobbing on her hip, smiling coyly at the police officer. The officer seemed unimpressed by her beauty. He uttered a few harsh questions, to which she shook her head in response. He turned and walked over to my house. Nashiema's eyes were fixed on mine, until her door fell shut.

"*Bonjour, Madame*." The officer greeted me in a most friendly way and studied my house.

"*Bonjour, Monsieur*, would you like to have a look inside?" I invited him in, hoping he would become my friend. In a country like Morocco, it was exceedingly helpful to make friends with a police officer.

He was very interested and spent a long time walking up and down. When we were standing on the top floor terrace, he said, "What a beautiful view towards the sea!"

"Yes," I agreed.

He looked down into the village.

"And over the village," he noticed.

I fiddled with the hem of my shirt.

"Have you seen Mohamed today?" he asked casually, throwing little bits of dried cement down onto the path.

"*Non, Monsieur*," I lied, feeling bad. Here I was, trying to make a new friend and during the first ten minutes of our conversation, I had already lied to him. I did not care about Mohamed, but I cared about Nashiema and Samir. Who would look after them, if Mohamed had to go to prison? Whatever he had done, he was still supplying his family with food and drink.

"Last week?"

"*Non, Monsieur*," I lied again.

Maybe we were not meant to become friends.

He was not friendly anymore.

"*Au revoir, Madame*," he said politely and left.

I watched the car turn and speed off. Can't be friends with everybody, I consoled myself. I somehow doubted he would ever come up to rescue me if I phoned in an emergency. Nashiema appeared in her yard and looked up at me. I discreetly put my thumb up and returned to my work.

Digby and Yassin were concreting floors, while Bilal continued plastering. He moved in slow motion all day long and spent a considerable amount of time smoothing over the ceiling of the bedroom. I could not figure out what was wrong. As he insisted he had got over his gastric flu, I was starting to suspect that he was trying to prolong his employment. With Yassin's help, I asked him, how long he thought he needed to finish the job. He thought six days. We agreed on four days, although I believed that two days would have been enough.

After the unusual rainy and cold spell, the weather changed. It became sunny and hot. One morning I woke up to complete silence. There was no sign of Yasmina sweeping the path next to my van and clucking for the dogs. I rushed to the window and looked out. The door to Yasmina's dwelling had gone. Instead of the cheerful blue and white metal door, a wall of grey breeze blocks greeted me, held together by dark lines of wet cement. I walked around my house towards the school to find the door was now on the other side of her house opening onto the path leading to the square. What a difference it made to my property! Now I could have a piece of land adjacent to my house. Nobody would walk up and down anymore right under my window or have unintelligible conversations with dogs and other animals. The relentless sweeping around my feet would also stop.

I did not have to wait long for Cherifa to turn up and invite me to buy the path from her. She appeared with Moulham. I was surprised to see that money not only divides but also unites families.

"*Trois mille cinq cent dirham,*" Moulham translated arduously.

Cherifa nodded in agreement and flashed her metal tooth. I was inclined to agree immediately, having already planned a cosy private courtyard with flowers and a home for my camper van.

However, the path did not only give access to Yasmina's house as I had discovered just in time. Tucked in the middle of the cluster was a small piece of land, owned by a French couple. It was surrounded by a low brick wall, which indicated that building was in progress. The only way to get to the land was via Yasmina's path. Or via Moulham's garden.

"*Mekin mushkeel, Madame. Pas de problème,*" Moulham waved his small hand as if irritated by a fly. "You buy, *Madame.* No worry."

I could imagine Moulham charging outrageous tolls whenever the poor French couple wanted to get to their house and forcing them to buy *litros* in bulk every time they went to Agadir.

"I must think about it, Cherifa, *réfléchir*." I tipped the sides of my head with my fingers.

It was too hot to do any effective thinking. After the coolness of the past week, the sudden heat paralysed me, whereas my neighbours, accustomed to scorching temperatures, were carefully peeling off the first of several layers of garments. At ten thirty in the evening, it was still twenty-eight degrees Celsius. I was too hot in my van.

When I woke up in the morning after an unrefreshing sleep, the temperature was three degrees higher. Exhausted, I crawled out and into the coolness of my house.

Bilal worked slowly, so slowly, that Digby became annoyed. I had to bribe Bilal with four packets of Casa cigarettes and two tins of sardines to finish the ceiling of the living room.

It was a hot evening and I did not want to spend it cooped up in my van. I wondered if I should go and see Yassin in this café, but I had not visited him for such a long time that I felt unable to surmount the wall, which was standing between us now. I was ashamed to admit that a certain amount of childish sulkiness on my side had allowed this to happen. I had hidden behind "being busy" and "no time to visit Yassin" until the rift between us had become so great that I had started avoiding the area around his café altogether.

I was also confused about the recent discovery that my feelings for him were not purely platonic.

I missed my friend. I missed his hospitality, his sharing his food with me or on special days cooking my favourite dishes. I missed our conversations, our hilarious jokes and his surprisingly mature and wise philosophies on life.

"Oh, bother," I thought, drove to Taghazout, parked and soon entered the café.

Yassin was not there.

Mohamed, who was helping out, said, "Yassin – *a la maison*."

Yassin was at home. It was not meant to be then, not tonight at least. I returned to Taliouine.

A few days later, Cherifa and Moulham paid another visit.

"*Madame, vous voulez achetez*?" Moulham came straight to the point.

Cherifa, Moulham and I haggled for a while as it is the custom until we reached an agreement somewhere in between our ideas of the value of the land. Moulham wanted four *litros* for his generosity to let the French couple use his footpath.

"I can give you money, Moulham, but I cannot buy you any alcohol. It is not allowed," I repeated patiently.

"*C'est bien, Madame*," Moulham said.

It had almost become a ritual.

Not much later Cherifa returned.

"*Madame*," she said, waving me over to her house, where she squatted down in the shadow of the wall. I sat down next to her.

"*Ca va, Madame*?" Cherifa enquired, flossing her teeth with a thin stick.

"*Eyeh, shokran. La bes*, Cherifa?"

"*La bes, bejer*."

I wondered what she wanted. She was not like Nadah or Nashiema. She would never come over only for a chat.

We looked along the coast for a while.

I waited.

"*Deux cent dirham, Madame*."

The price for the path had gone up. And Moulham was not meant to know.

The next day I ordered Bilal and Digby to take a holiday. It was agreed that Cherifa and I would go to the notary to proceed with the purchase of the land. When I entered the courtyard of her house, I found not only Cherifa, but also Nashiema, Samir and Nadah getting ready to go out. The sisters were stuffing towels and clothes into large plastic bags. Samir, clad in a little light-blue combination with a faded Disney emblem, waved his arms excitedly, black curls bouncing.

"*Bonjour, Madame*," Nadah greeted me with a big smile. "*Hammam* Aourir, *Madame*," she added.

The colourful group bundled into my van, heaving bags, unpacking picnics of fruit and pancakes, and twittering and chatting without stopping. Nadah and Nashiema had never been inside my van. They balanced precariously while we bumped down the track and opened cupboard after cupboard to peep at my belongings. Every single thing was commented on, until after hitting a large pothole they fell over each other onto the bench and remained there, laughing, until I stopped the van in Aourir.

Nadah and Nashiema set off for the *Hammam* for their weekly bath, while Samir stayed with Cherifa. The three of us entered the notary's office.

Mr Abderrahim did not even ask for any papers. He had seen Moulham's papers last time and that seemed to be all he needed. And while everything was going so smoothly, Cherifa decided to push her luck.

She bent forwards. Her eyes shone, and while she talked, her voice became shrill. When she finished, the notary turned to me.

"*Madame*," he said. "You had a hole dug into the path?"

"Yes," I replied, shifting on my chair. Images of pregnant Mina on the bottom of my soak-away popped up.

"And where is it in relation to your house?"

"It is right outside, next to my front door."

Monsieur glanced at Cherifa. His expression wiped the smile off her face.

"Madame is asking you for payment for the hole you dug into the path, which she believes is her property."

My kind and friendly neighbours, never tired of milking me like a fat cow as soon as the opportunity occurred.

"How much?" I asked.

"*Madame, s'il vous plait!*" The notary leant forwards, scowling, his voice coloured with anger. "Two metres around the boundary of your house is your land. Whatever you do with it – do not give money to anyone. It is greed. I am sorry."

Cherifa looked out of the window.

We signed the contracts. I handed the money over to the notary. When I was about to whisk Cherifa off to Taghazout for the uninspiring process of certifying our signatures she firmly said: "*Oho!*"

Not today, Saturday, but next Wednesday, I learned. Another feast was looming: *Moharem*, the Muslim New Year. Nobody was going to work until the fete was over. Living in the mountains, this fact had escaped my awareness, or I would not have gone to the notary at all. By now, my visa had expired and I was tolerated in this country solely due to my provisional prolongation. A proper extension had not been granted yet. Any day I could be given the marching order. I did not want to deposit my money in the top drawer of Monsieur Abderrahim's desk for the undefined duration of my absence.

Contrary to Cherifa, I was quite sure that the town halls were open, as the whole of Aourir showed no signs of the nearing holiday. The small garages, shops and even the notary were a busy as usual. I urged to leave and drove with Cherifa and little Samir on the passenger seats first to Taghazout, where we found the town hall shut, and then to Agadir, where we also found the town hall shut. Cherifa had been right and I felt uncomfortable under her triumphant smirk.

In the shadow of a palm tree, a soldier was mopping his forehead with a handkerchief.

"*Monsieur!*" I leaned out of the window and gesticulated madly at the uniformed man.

He heaved himself up and strolled over.

"*Oui, Madame?*" He stared at my two companions.

"*Le mairie, Monseiur, c'est femer aujourd'hui?*"

"Of course it is shut, *Madame*. It is a holiday."

Cherifa giggled.

"But I need someone to certify our signatures today!"

"No problem, *Madame*, you have to go to the police station *1ˢᵗ Arrondissement*, where you will find help. Turn right and it will be on the left side."

"*Shokran, Monsieur.*"

I smiled at Cherifa.

Soon the three of us piled into the bleak whitewashed police station. The officer behind the desk took my papers.

"No problem, *Madame*."

A second officer appeared, filling the room with an air of authority and fear. After a short conversation, the first officer, who seemed to have shrunk, handed the papers back with an apologetic smile.

"But why can't you do it?" I asked desperately.

"Please leave, *Madame*," he ordered.

Cherifa sniggered.

What a drag coming out all the way to Agadir on such a dry and hot day! And with little Samir! He looked very tired and exhausted, and I felt a pang of guilt. I bought bottles of water and some fresh oranges from a stall. In the car I cut them in half and offered them to Cherifa and Samir, who greedily sucked the juice.

Back in Aourir I dropped Cherifa, whose turn it was to visit the *Hammam*, and picked up Nashiema. Moulham was with her, revving up his moped.

"Taghazout *tajine*?" he asked.

I agreed, thinking that a little celebration would be very nice for Nashiema, forgetting that women did not visit the cafes in Taghazout. More than that, Nashiema was so frightened that Mohamed would see her in the village that she squatted down with Samir in a shady pathway near the café.

I could not eat anything, thinking of Nashiema all the time. How could I have been so thoughtless! We should have gone straight up to Taliouine. I was relieved when Moulham struck up a conversation with three fishermen. I took bread and two bottles of water and left Moulham to his tajine. I bought bananas and chocolate and joined Nashiema. Together we sat on the dirty ground and shared the food and drink.

"I am sorry, Nashiema, *je suis désolée. Excuse moi*," I said.

"*Mekin mushkeel, Madame*," Nashiema smiled and watched Samir play amongst discarded tins and plastic bottles.

When we arrived back in Taliouine, Nadah was outside. In the seclusion of a wall she was beaming at a young Moroccan man.

His name was Hafid, and he lived in one of the neighbouring villages. Hafid sported a constant frown and did not smile often. Yet, the rough features made him attractive - for some women. My friend Yassin simply called him a thug.

When he saw us arriving, he quickly disappeared leaving behind a glowing Nadah. She never glowed like that after Philippe's visits, I thought. For once she was not holding on to her mobile phone. The battery was flat anyway. Nadah had even stopped asking me to charge it on my car battery.

"Do you like Hafid? *L'amour*?" I asked, after she had hooked one arm through mine.

Nadah, who was very direct and usually never minded being spoken to in the same way, blushed and giggled.

"What about Philippe?"

Nadah shrugged her shoulders and rearranged her scarf with one hand, pushing some escaped black strands back into their prison.

"Philippe – *beaucoup d'argent*!" I tempted her, explanatorily rubbing the tips of my fingers.

Nadah laughed.

"*Oui*," she answered slowly, "*mais – Hafid – l'amour*."

Nadah was not materialistic and I could imagine that she would be able to let the financial chance of her lifetime slip through her fingers in order to marry a thug, because she was in love with him. If she was allowed to, that was. Cherifa would be in fits if she knew.

I did not blame Nadah. How long was she meant to wait for indecisive Philippe? It was much nicer anyway to marry someone for love rather than money.

My neighbour Yassin invited me for a house-warming *tajine* in his new family home: one room for the little family, with a tiny yard, where Mina cooked. I was worried about the roof, which still was no more than a plastic sheet with sand on the top and a few stones to hold it down.

Hassan had painted the room indigo blue. A fluffy pink bunny, probably a present from a tourist, was fixed onto the wall as decoration. A bright green plastic ivy "grew" in the corner. A cable ran along the walls, held up by the occasional nail and leading to a single naked light bulb which dangled from the ceiling. A fat spider sat motionless above the door.

Hassan pointed at the mattresses on the floor and we sat down. Mina appeared with a clay dish and placed it on the wooden table.

We dipped our pieces of bread into a hot *tajine*, which tasted of chicken and coriander. Afterwards Yassin played on his drums while Mina sang. Little Jalal was so tired he fell asleep leaning forwards over the low table. His hand was still clutching a piece of bread.

Chapter Thirty

Moharem, the Muslim New Year, was celebrated with the slaughter of a cow. An all-male crowd gathered around the mosque on the far hill, where Lahcen from Ait Tabbia had the honour cutting the cow's throat. The rest of the day was spent with visits between families. The women were singing and their high-pitched voices trailed through the village. They were accompanied by the metallic clacking of the *garagab*, the Moroccan castanets, and the sound of *tam tam* and *bandir*, the traditional Berber drums. All day long the smell of cooking lingered over the village.

Moulham invited me to share a *tajine* in the evening, to which I contributed potatoes, vegetables and Coke. It was a peaceful night. The full moon lit up the yard, and I watched ants the size of small grasshoppers walking in a busy line across the uneven concrete. The dim shine of candles and flickering fires fell into the courtyard through the different doors. Latifa and Fatim, Moulham's granddaughters, chased each other, laughing and singing as they jumped over shadows.

"*Donnez-moi un peu!*" Moulham whispered, when I left.

He had made it a habit to ask me for money. Maybe it was time to rethink our relationship.

The following day, like the day after *Aid el Kebir*, Taliouine was deserted. Everyone had gone to visit relatives in the neighbourhood. A thin layer of fog lingered above the village, and I pottered around in the house, did some minor plastering without enthusiasm or talent and generally felt bored and lonely.

The scrunching of tyres on dry mud announced the rare arrival of a car in the village. I looked over the terrace wall, hoping that it was not the police again, then quickly pulled back.

It was Philippe on the way to his in-laws-to-be. Did he not know that nobody was at home? And most of all, has he not noticed that Nadah had fallen for Hafid-the-thug? I slumped onto my chair, wondering if I should go down to the beach or wait until the fog had lifted, when I heard a knock at my door. My heart started to thump.

"Don't get your hopes up," I said to myself. "He will want to know where everybody has gone."

I skipped down the stairs - my heartbeat was beating like a mad Geiger counter - and opened the door.

"Oh hi," I said, watching a lizard disappear under a stone. "If you are looking for Nadah – they have all gone out, visiting relatives. It is their New Year."

"I know," Philippe grinned. "I have been living here for quite a while. I knew that nobody was at home." The car keys ran through his fingers like worry beads. "I thought … I mean, maybe it is not a good idea … but I am going to Marrakech for a couple of days, and I wondered if you would like to come." His eyes scanned the wall of my house.

I stared at him in disbelief. I was offered a weekend-break in one of the most magical cities with the most delectable man around? Me? Had I won some kind of radio quiz – the lottery – was I dreaming?

Philippe misread my hesitation. Scratching the side of his nose, he said, "I did not want to offend you. I meant just as friends, you know. I thought you might be as bored as I am by all those family holidays. Maybe you have different plans. I am sorry." He tensed and stepped back.

"Wait here! And give me five minutes!" I shot past him.

I dashed into my camper van and rummaged through the cupboards like a burglar, throwing toothbrush, toothpaste, soap, brush, eyeliner, my favourite dress, a pair of leggings, underwear and a jumper into a bag. Then I grabbed my passport and purse.

I jumped out of the van, locked it, rushed past my house, locked it and had caught up with Philippe before he had time to regret and leave without me.

"I'm ready," I beamed, my body clammy and nervous like a teenager's.

"Let's go." Philippe said with a wide smile and opened the passenger door for me.

I could not remember anyone doing this before and, feeling pleasantly spoilt, climbed inside. Philippe started the engine. The air-conditioning purred softly.

"Philippe, before we go, can I ask you something?"

"Yes, of course."

"What is going on between you and Nadah? I can't possibly go with you, if you are involved with her. Not even as a friend. She is my neighbour, and I like her very much."

"If I was involved with Nadah, I would never have asked you to come with me. Not even as a friend." Philippe loosened the handbrake.

"Right, off we go then," I said, satisfied and eager to get away.

Slowly Philippe drove down the dusty track. I was so excited, I could have rubbed my hands, danced around on my seat or sung a song, but I contented myself with looking out of the window and humming quietly.

We reached Taghazout and found the usually bustling fishing village deserted, except for one person who nearly ran into the car. Philippe braked hard. It was my friend Yassin, and the unexpected sight startled me. He stared at me through the window. I smiled uncertainly, but he did not smile back. Then we were past. I watched him in the wing mirror staring after the car until we were out of sight.

"Yassin!" Philippe murmured, when his wave remained unacknowledged. "I wonder what is wrong with him."

"I have no idea," I said, feeling flustered.

Outside Agadir, we turned inland and circled round the ever-expanding city. Several shantytowns of sub-standard mud dwellings strung together by washing lines and deadly electricity cables still littered the dusty plain. The inhabitants were in the process of being relocated to newly erected apartment blocks. After that, the slums would be bulldozed into a thing of the past. The new king was fighting poverty.

We left the Souss valley and started to climb the foothills of the High Atlas. The road became winding and narrow. Lorries and buses crowded the road, trying to overtake each other in hair-raising manoeuvres. We drove along in silence, my hands resting on the soft cotton cover of my seat. Philippe was concentrating on the traffic, while I, for once not driving, looked out of the window.

The road curved around hilltop villages with houses the colour of washed-out carmine, blending almost seamlessly into the reddish background. Had I been driving, I might not even have noticed them. Now I was craning my neck as not to miss a single detail.

With increasing altitude the fog grew thinner until it gave way to a clear blue sky. A few clouds clung to the peaks like cotton wool smoke to the chimney of a gingerbread house.

The rusty red of the iron rich soil contrasted with olive coloured Argan trees and shrubs. The distant hills looked almost purple in the sunlight. We passed simple dwellings with traditional stonework and more recent extensions made from breezeblocks, painted pink or white. Stones were piled up along the way, maybe to build a wall. Spiky cactus plants with red-orange fruit protected private land like barbed wire.

Red and brown hills with dots of green wherever I looked. Black goats frisked about by the side of the road, guarded by a man clad in a matching black *djellaba*.

A mosque on the hilltop, a village spreading down the hillside. A man and a donkey were working in a field. The

232

donkey pulled a wooden plough. More dwellings flew past, powdery pink against brilliant blue.

We were still climbing. I avoided looking at the road because many Moroccan drivers were reckless, without fear. Fate lay in Allah's hands. If He wanted an accident to happen, it was not man's job to interfere.

Soon we were surrounded by mountains. The colours changed. Soft rolling taupe hills, trees dabbed with pink and white blossom.

A woman was collecting herbs into a rugged wicker basket. She was wrapped in brightly coloured layers of fabric, her hair hidden under a sunflower yellow scarf. She waved as we rushed past.

A villa, luxurious almost, on its own, backing onto the road. A woman looked down from a balcony. Her headscarf had golden trimmings and coins dangling from the seams. She looked sad.

In the middle of nowhere, a man sat by the side of the road. Why? Behind him green sprouting fields. The colour looked unreal.

Chameleon villages huddled on the hillsides.

From time to time, I studied Philippe's profile, a perfectly sized nose, long eyelashes, smiling lips. His eyes were fixed onto the road.

"If you want water, there is a bottle on the back seat. And some biscuits, if you are hungry," he said.

I turned round and got hold of both. I opened the bottle and handed it over to him. He took several deep gulps and gave it back to me. I drank greedily too, thinking how intimate it was to share a bottle of water. We ate some biscuits.

Soon afterwards, I nodded off and woke with a start when the car stopped. Sleepily I opened my eyes.

"Are we there?" I looked around.

"No, not yet, but I need a coffee and a rest." Philippe turned the engine off.

We had stopped outside a transport café, sharing the car park with a number of lorries. In Morocco lorries were not just commercial vehicles. They were works of art, painted pink, blue or green with symbols, Arabic patterns and words like *Love* or *Peace* written over it. Inside the cabin, the dashboard and floor was covered in bits of carpets and rugs. Colourful trimmings framed the windows and gold-edged curtains fluttered in the wind.

We sat down on shabby orange plastic chairs, shaded from the sun by a wisteria plant, and ordered two coffees from the young waiter.

I was wide-awake and, not being used to not driving, did not fancy another hour of sitting doing nothing. Soon we would reach Chichaoua and with it the end of the mountains. From then on there would only be flat plain to look at. I wondered if Philippe would let me drive his car.

"Shall I drive?" I stirred more sugar into the strong coffee.

"Yes."

"Pardon?"

"I said yes."

"Oh, all right then." I looked at him. "Philippe, you are collecting brownie points."

"I am nice," he laughed, green eyes sparkling and holding on to mine.

Not only have I always had a weakness for French accents, but also for kind men. I got up quickly. Fancying somebody or actually coupling up was not on my agenda. It scared me. It would destroy my carefully constructed world, where I felt safe and indestructible. I had not been "with someone" for ages and did not know how to do relationships anymore. The idea of flirting sent me into a nervous flurry.

While Philippe was looking for a toilet, I started to wonder where we were going to spend the night. Philippe seemed to know where he was heading. I was astonished to find myself so unquestioning and trusting, even relieved not having to make decisions all the time.

Driving Philippe's comfortable and safe car was an exhilarating experience for me. The road had been descending for a while. At the foot of the High Atlas, we reached Imi-n-

Tanoute, too vast to be called a village, too small to be a town. Roadside cafes and stalls flew past. Afterwards, the road was almost straight and the traffic eased.

"Philippe, where will we stay tonight?" I asked but did not get an answer.

Philippe had fallen asleep. There was a tiny smile on his lips. His hair, painted golden by the Moroccan sun, had grown since I saw him first in the launderette. A stray strand had fallen over his face. I wanted to brush it back into its place, then swallowed and gripped the steering wheel tighter.

It was afternoon when we approached Marrakech. Philippe woke up. Out of the corner of my eye, I saw him stretch. I focussed on the road ahead.

"Did you have a good sleep?"

"I did," Philippe answered, trying to figure out where we were. "In fact, I enjoyed it. It is a rare opportunity."

Yes, yes, us lone travellers. I could tell you a thing or two about that, I thought.

"Where will we stay?" I repeated.

He yawned.

"Friends of mine have a little house in the medina of Marrakech. They live in France and come down here once or twice a year. I have the key and can use the house whenever I want. In return, I make sure that everything is all right. I do come up here quite often, actually, at least once a month."

"You are lucky," I said, imagining being able to nip over to Marrakech every other week.

He looked at me.

"Yes. Because you are here."

I swallowed again and glued my eyes back onto the tarmac.

I stopped at the next lay-by to let Philippe take over. For once, I did not have to battle with Marrakech's late afternoon traffic. I would actually be able to see something of this town other than the murderous race of cars, bicycles and carts.

Before I could open the door, Philippe took my hand.

"I am sorry, I offended you."

"You didn't." I watched a couple chug past on an ancient moped; a small infant was sandwiched between them.

"Yes, I did. Don't misunderstand, please. I am glad that you are here, just as a friend. I would never exploit that."

My hand fitted snugly into his dry warm one.

"No offence taken." I listened to my cheerful voice and detected a nuance of regret.

For a long time, we approached the town centre on a straight dual carriageway with badly coordinated traffic lights. The roads were lined with new developments. Villas and luxury apartments had been erected since King Mohamed V took over the regime. Acres of smooth terracotta and dark pink habitations were sitting in almost complete silence. The Moroccan equivalent of *For Sale* signs in the windows, they were waiting to be bought and filled with life.

Spring is a beautiful season to experience in Morocco. The air is clear, even in a congested town like Marrakesh, and the colours are bright and fresh. Plants and trees are of a wholesome green and sprout colourful blossom. Orange trees are strewn with white flowers oozing a pungent scent. The palm trees wave healthy looking leaves in the cooling afternoon wind.

We circled round the walled medina until Philippe pulled onto a vast car park near one of the gates leading into the old town.

"We are there. This is the gate Bab Doukkala."

He turned the engine off. A Moroccan man appeared by his window. A blue scarf was slung around his head like a turban, the *tagilmust* of the Tuareg nomads. He smiled and exposed three yellow teeth, like stalagmites in a dark grotto. Laughing, Philippe wound the window down and stretched out his hand.

"Mohamed!"

Mohamed grabbed Philippe's hand with his weather and labour worn ones and patted it amicably. They went through the ritual of greeting and enquiries about the rest of the family. In Berber.

"Kate, this is Mohamed. He always looks after my car, when I am here."

In Morocco, it is a good idea to have someone trustworthy guard one's car.

"*Bonjour, Madame.*"

Mohamed stretched his arm into the car to shake my hand. His callused palm felt rough on mine.

"*Bonjour, Monsieur.*"

We disappeared through a keyhole-shaped archway into a maze of dusty narrow streets. Philippe strode on purposefully; left turn, right turn, across the small square, under the arch, left turn, right turn, left turn. Not long, and I was completely lost.

For the last ten minutes, I had seen walls and doors and occasionally a person, staring at us curiously. There were small shops, selling bread and cakes, vegetables and fruit. A group of young girls turned round the corner, chatting excitedly and balancing trays of freshly baked bread and biscuits.

"*Bonjour Madame – Monsieur,*" they sang.

"They come from the communal bakery," Philippe explained. "The dough is made at home and taken to the communal oven to be baked."

"*Madame,*" one of the girls called after us.

I turned round.

She lowered her tray and held it out to me.

"*Tiens, Madame.*"

"*Shokran,*" I said, taking a biscuit covered in coconut flakes.

Giggling, the girls walked off.

"Here, have a bit." I broke a piece off for Philippe. "It is delicious." I jumped to one side to let a donkey cart pass. "I did not know you spoke Berber."

"Only a bit," Philippe answered, pulling himself along an invisible threat, which led us through the thicket of the medina to a tatty blue metal door, one amongst hundreds. He fumbled for the keys and unlocked the door. It swung wide open. Philippe put his hand on my back and pushed me gently inside.

Through an archway, I entered a courtyard, dimly lit by the last of the daylight. There was a zigzag pattern of blue and white tiles on the floor. In the middle of the courtyard, I could make out a tiled basin, a fountain. Pale pink rose petals were floating on the surface. Pots of various sizes and different shades of terracotta and blue were grouped in the corners, holding a firework of flowers. The sweet scent of orange blossom filled the air.

Wooden doors, unpainted and ornately carved, led to several rooms. My eyes wandered upwards. There was another floor. Rooms were leading off a kind of veranda, which circled around the courtyard. Flowers and greenery were trailing down from the wooden balustrade like curtains. Above, a square of blue and reddish pink sky gleamed with pre-sunset intensity.

"It is so beautiful," I said. "Not surprising you pop in every other week. It is a paradise."

"Yes, it is. Every time I come here, I am stunned."

Phillip fiddled with hidden switches. The courtyard, which had slowly been fading away with the daylight, glowed warmly. The palms cast filigree shadows onto the whitewashed walls. Water started trickling down the fountain.

"Fatna, a neighbour, looks after the house, when nobody is here. She waters the flowers. Usually, I phone her brother before I arrive. Then she buys bread and vegetables from the money I had left here the time before, so that I don't need to go shopping," Philippe explained.

In one of the corners almost hidden by the long, slim leaves of a banana plant, I discovered a seating area with big spice-coloured cushions strewn all over the floor and a low wooden table with a cast iron lantern.

"We should leave as soon as possible to get to Djemaa el Fna. What do you think?"

"Oh, yes of course, let's go straight away," I said with a last longing glance at the comfortable cushions. I did not want to miss Marrakech's famous square and its daily transition into an enormous open-air restaurant.

"Let me first show you your room. There is time for a wash or change, if you want. Five minutes." Philippe smiled and beckoned me to follow him.

"You know I don't take long," I said, following him up the steep staircase.

The noises of the medina floated through the yard: the beeping of small mopeds, the braying of donkeys, a jumble of Berber conversations, singing and drumming in the background.

We walked along the balcony. I stopped and looked over the balustrade into the courtyard.

Philippe opened one of the doors.

"Here is your room."

It was a small whitewashed rectangle. Red cement tiles covered the floor. I took in the single bed with a colourful throw, a kind of desk with a chair and a small stone bench lined with thick foam cushions – the Berber style sofa. Like the other rooms, it featured a window with a mosaic of green and yellow tinted glass, opening into the courtyard.

"If you don't like it, you can choose another one. This one is made up. We would have to change the bedding..."

"Philippe, I love it." I interrupted gently, making a mental note to create a room like this back in my house.

There was a bathroom further along the balcony. Ten minutes later I was back downstairs, showered and clad in my favourite orange pinkish ankle length dress, pink leggings to cover my legs, in case they peeped out through the slit at the back, a light pink jumper to cover my arms.

Philippe appeared a minute later, wearing faded blue jeans and a white t-shirt. He carried a sweatshirt, mint green, to match his eyes.

"You look beautiful," he said, took my hand and kissed it gently. His hair was still wet, and he smelled delicious.

'You, too,' I thought. Embarrassed, but delighted I wriggled away and headed for the door.

We did not have to go far to Djemaa el Fna. There was little time left until sunset. The square was packed with people, mainly Moroccans, milling around and watching the performances. Snake charmers wrapped a few metres of snake around terrified onlookers and charged ten dirham for a photo. Five-year olds were boxing with oversized leather gloves, while

239

their trainers/coaches/fathers took bets. Musicians in colourful traditional garments sang melancholic melodies from the mountains, their faces reflecting the orange shine of the fires lit in disused oil drums. Women in colourful wraps applied delicate henna patterns to outstretched hands.

We listened to a storyteller, an old man with a weather beaten face and a long grey beard. Speaking in a low, melodious voice, he took a white dove out of a small wooden cage. He cupped his hands around the bird and lifted its head to his lips. After he had spoken, he released the bird into the sky. The dove circled above the square. Higher and higher it went, a shiny white dot against the orange sunset.

Finally, it returned to land on the storyteller's shoulder. Again the old man cupped his hands around the dove. He bent down, listening to the story, which the bird had brought back from its journey through the sky, and passed it on to his audience. Children and adults were equally captivated, listening to the old man with their mouths open. I was enthralled, caught in a dream, in a fairytale. This was the only way I could explain the fact that my hand had found its way into Philippe's welcomingly warm one.

The dove was released again and returned one more time, with a last story. There was no sound other than the old man's voice. The noises of the square seemed to belong to a different world. It was magic, and all the time I felt my hand in Philippe's and pleasant sensations running through my body.

The storyteller had finished. He gently put the dove back into its cage. Tomorrow it would fly again, looking for another story, *insha'allah*.

Feet shuffled and the enchanted audience dispersed. Philippe and I were left, standing hand in hand, not knowing what to do or say next. I pulled my hand out of Philippe's and pointed to the other side of the square.

"Look, Philippe. Let's go over to watch."

I walked ahead, putting space between us, feeling a mixture of fear and excitement.

The far end of the square was bathed in gas-fired bright lights. Steam rose from huge pots and barbecues. Hundreds of hands speedily carried wooden benches, tables, cutlery, plates, bowls and glasses, food and soft drinks, bunches of mint and coriander, vegetables and fruit, meat and fish.

We were excited like children, and there was no awkwardness between us when we reached the food stalls.

"Let's eat *harira* first," suggested Philippe, steering me through the crowds of people already gathered around his favourite soup stall. *Harira*, a thick soup with lentils, meat and tomatoes is usually eaten during Ramadan after sunset to break the fasting day.

Philippe ordered two bowls of soup and we carried them carefully to the nearest bench. It was already filled with people tucking into their soups. We squeezed in, placing our bowls on the narrow table between us. I eyed the wooden spoons we had been given, imagining a pack of malicious bacteria smiling at me from the natural wood.

'So what?' I thought and I started eating. Parsley, coriander, ginger and saffron hit my taste buds and exploded into a firework of flavours, foreign and exotic. Stories from *Arabian Nights* shot through my mind. I laughed out loud; it was so exhilarating.

Newcomers clutching bowls and spoons pushed us further along the bench. There was not much room under the table and I felt my legs being kicked and nudged until they were engulfed by Philippe's. I spooned the soup into my mouth, but I could not look at Philippe in case he noticed how much it unsettled me. My legs where tingling and burning in response.

"Let's move on," he said, as soon as we had finished. "There are so many people waiting for a place to sit, and there is still so much more to see. And to eat."

We returned the bowls and spoons, which joined others in a plastic bowl of cloudy water, and strolled on. Each food stall/restaurant had a mouth-watering display. Brochettes and meatballs were resting on beds of coriander, until chosen by a punter and flung onto the grill. Fish were sorted by size and colour and arranged like rainbows, framed by bunches of parsley. Lines of lemons resembled gigantic necklaces. There were tomatoes and lettuce, olives and cucumbers, fried aubergines and spinach salad. Towers of round breads in amidst mountains of prawns, octopus and mussels. Strong scents and colours were predominant. There was no subtlety. It was far removed from Moroccan's usual palette of fading pastels.

The long narrow tables, decked with white paper, featured bottles of soft drinks, to which guests could help themselves. We walked up and down, almost torn apart by touts dressed in white jackets, thrusting written menus into our hands and trying to persuade us to eat at "*chez* Yassin" or "*Frères* Mohamed".

Wavering between fish and meat, stew and steak, brochettes and sausages and chicken we ended up sampling nearly everything, wandering, sitting down, eating, drinking, chatting and watching. One thing I could not bring myself to try was offal, and I noticed that the eateries offering cows' udders and sheep's brains were frequented by Moroccans rather than foreign visitors.

The musicians in the square continued to play and sing throughout the evening.

After hours, the frantic cooking, grilling and serving slowed down. People were saturated.

"Try this," Philippe said at last, grabbing my hand and pulling me to a small stall on the edge of the spectacle. "It is called *la teinte*."

The stallholder served two tea glasses filled with a hot red liquid. It was a spicy tea with a slight Christmassy flavour of cinnamon and ginger. A plate with round marble sized cakes accompanied the tea, peppered with ginger and almost as soft as fresh dough.

"Delicious," I managed to say between two marbles, "just like Christmas."

Philippe laughed. "I like it for the same reason."

Away from the noise and the buzzing of the last hours I started to feel tired and yawned.

"Let's go now, shall we?" Philippe said.

I nodded. He put his arm around me and led me back to the house.

Again, we stepped through the blue metal door into the paradisiacal courtyard. Again, as if by magic the lights came on and the water started to tinkle. I was tempted to sink onto the comfortable cushions in the corner, but felt safer going straight to bed. I turned to Philippe.

"It was such a lovely evening, Philippe, thank you. You can't imagine what it means to me to be here. It is pure magic."

He gently brushed my cheek with his finger.

"You are very appreciative. I enjoyed the evening, too. Usually, I don't have half as much fun."

We both laughed.

"Right, I am going to bed now," I yawned demonstratively, bent forwards and kissed Philippe on the cheek.

He pulled me into a cosy hug.

"*Bonne nuit*. Sleep well."

I crawled into my bed. Before dozing off, I heard Philippe turn the lights and the water off and go to bed, too.

Chapter Thirty One

A ray of sunlight sneaked into my room through a tiny window in the wall. I opened my eyes without moving. I was still half immersed in a beautiful dream and did not want to wake up. My eyes circled round the room without knowing where I was. I heard muffled street noises but could not make out which street they were coming from. The air was different to Taliouine, denser, with a faint whiff of diesel fumes. I heard steps outside the bedroom door, fading away, down a staircase. A door opened. A series of clatters and bangs drifted through my walls, the sound of somebody busying himself in a kitchen. My heart produced a few extra beats. Philippe was making breakfast. I sat up. It had not been a dream.

I jumped out of bed and rushed to the bathroom. Showered and dressed, I ran downstairs. The courtyard glistened in the clear morning sunlight. From the middle of the yard I looked up at the flawless bright blue square above me. I remained like this for a long time.

"*Bonjour*, Kate, did you sleep well?"

I turned round. Philippe was leaning at one of the pillars outside the kitchen, a tea towel slung over his shoulder, his hands buried in his trouser pockets.

"Yes, thank you, and you? Let me help you."

245

Together we made breakfast. The carved wooden table was soon laden with fresh bread, apricot jam, honey, butter and continental coffee.

"What would you like to do today?" Philippe spread crumbs everywhere in true French manner. "I know it is difficult to answer, because there is so much and we only have little time. What do you like best in Marrakech?"

The vibrant souk, the mythical medina, the traditional cafes, the scents of bread, cakes and kefta, the chanting coming from the mosque, the fast chatter of the people, the intensity of colours, the setting sun painting fire onto the crenulated town walls, the snow–capped High Atlas towering above.

"How about the gardens?" I answered, remembering explosions of subtropical vegetation and palm trees heavy with dates.

We left the house and mastered the maze of narrow streets, which were humming with activity. A group of young girls rushed past on their way to school, dressed in white smocks, clutching satchels. Stalls had opened and a colourful display of *baboushes*, jewellery, brass and ceramic lined the streets. Men in *djellabas* were sweeping away the dust of the night, polishing plates, lanterns, candleholders, then arranged themselves on low wooden chairs on the lookout for punters, while consuming litres of sweet mint tea.

"*Madame*! *Monsieur*! Come! Look! Verrrry cheap! Special price today!"

We slipped out of the medina through one of the town gates. A petit taxi, Marrakesh's ochre-coloured city transport, took us to the Menara Gardens. It is an olive grove rather than a flower garden and features a water-filled basin the size of an Olympic swimming pool. The Menzeh, a tiny ornate summerhouse, is sitting at the far end of the basin, with the High Atlas towering in the background.

The air was fresh and clear – a perfect spring day. The snow-capped peaks were clearly visible. As the surface of the water was undisturbed by wind, the reflection of the mountains and the Menzeh was razor-sharp. We strolled around the basin until we had the best view and sat down on the stonewall

"It is a perfect day to come here," I said.

"It is. I have not often seen the mountains as clear as this," Philippe agreed.

For a long time we said nothing, both absorbed in the double display of the scenery. Being with Philippe was just like being with myself, but without the lonely bit.

Philippe took my hand and played absentmindedly with my fingers. A wave of heat ran through my body. I secretly glanced at him, but his eyes were fixed on the mountains. He seemed to be worlds away.

There was nobody but us. It was peaceful, quiet. Warm. I felt like rolling on my side like a dog with a big sigh and stretch out in the sun.

Philippe turned his face towards me. His eyes caught mine and held them. I wanted to take my eyes off him, make a light-hearted joke, return to the view, get a grip, but I couldn't. I sat on the wall, paralysed, staring into Philippe's eyes and feeling something beyond control welling up inside me.

"I feel so good being with you." Philippe gripped my hand tightly. His voice seemed to come from far away.

"Me too," I said, trying to keep a mayhem of emotions under control.

His eyes were beautiful, light green in the sunlight, almost too big for his face, with long curved eyelashes.

It felt like light years until we kissed. A gigantic wave closed over me. Philippe covered my mouth with gentle kisses, my cheeks and then pulled me into a tight hug. He felt so wonderful, so made for me. I fitted perfectly into his embrace and lay there, listening to our hearts beating.

Later Philippe said: "It would be better to go now. It is getting too hot."

Confused, I sat up, feeling for the first time the red-hot midday sun on me.

Holding each other's hands, we walked back through the olive groves. The rest of the day passed in a haze. The beautiful gardens of the Hotel Mamounia, oranges and grapefruits on trees, lunch in the shade, the exquisite garden of Majorelle, subtropical and tranquil. The only thing, which penetrated through the haze, was Philippe's presence. Philippe's arms around me, his hand in my hand, his lips on my lips, on my cheeks, furtive kisses, a bench in the garden.

All of a sudden, Philippe jumped up and pulled me with him. We left the garden, found a taxi and silently drove back to the ramparts, made our way back to the house, unlocked the door, went inside.

With his foot Philippe pushed the door shut, while his hands cupped my face. The pressure of his hands increased, his thumbs were brushing my lips, parting them. I felt burning hot as if I was on fire. He was watching me, teasing me, playing with my face, my lips. His face was only inches away from mine, his lips parted.

With a sigh, his mouth descended on mine, greedily, tongues touching before lips, passionately, starved, urgently. It was like an eruption of volcanoes, like all the fireworks of the world together, earthquake, nuclear explosion.

When we surfaced again, it was nearly dark in the house. The sun had set.

Philippe reached the wall behind me and switched the lights and the water fountain on again.

He smiled at me, then buried his head in my hair, slung his arms around me and whispered: "*Ma belle!*"

He whisked me off to his favourite restaurant, where we shared a plate of couscous.

After the plate had been cleared away, Philippe took my hand and said, "I have not been with anyone since my divorce."

No wonder we had clashed together with such a force. After my disastrous marriage I had never entered the dating market again.

"Tell me about Nadah."

Philippe took a sip of mint tea. "There is not much to say. As I told you, I have known the family for years. Lahcen, my sister's boyfriend, is Cherifa's nephew. Cherifa wants to marry

Nadah off and decided that I would make a perfect match for her. I did consider it a couple of years ago, when I was tired of being alone. But there is no point. I don't love Nadah, and she doesn't love me. I never proposed to her. It is purely in Cherifa's imagination."

"How do you know she does not love you?" I thought back to the evening when I saw Nadah beaming at Hafid-the-thug.

"Nadah has been in love with someone from a different village for a long time, but Cherifa would never allow her to marry him. She does not think him good enough for Nadah. But in the end she will come round to it. I like Nadah and letting Cherifa believe that we would get married one day gives her a bit more freedom."

"You are covering up for her, when she is with him?" I stared at him.

Philippe laughed.

"No, my friendship with Nadah doesn't go that far. I just did not tell Cherifa that there would not be a marriage. I did not have a reason to tell her. I will speak to her now, though. I don't want it to be an awkward situation for you."

I had to pull back. It was too early for commitments. I was not ready for complications of this kind, with my neighbours, with my inner life. I could just suggest to Philippe that we should forget what had happened, that we could stay friends. After all, there had been only a few kisses. I might just get away with it.

Or not? The protective wall I had so arduously constructed around me had been effortlessly demolished today and my world was shattered. But I was not distraught. On the contrary, I was happy. I was so incredibly happy.

Philippe took hold of both my hands.

"*Ma belle.*" Something in his voice made me look up.

"What is it?"

"I have to go to France tomorrow."

To my surprise I felt a lump in the back of my throat. Seconds ago I was trying to find a way out. Now my heart was thumping because I wanted him so badly. Found and lost, I thought, all within minutes.

"Forever?"

Philippe laughed. "I need to go back for two weeks to sort out some business affairs. I had planned to go from here, not knowing that I would actually pluck up the courage to ask you to come to Marrakech with me." He squeezed my hands and leant forwards. "Please come with me to France, if you are free."

I smiled unhappily. "I am not free, unfortunately, as you know. I am building a house. My people will already be wondering where I am and what has happened to me."

We set off early the next morning. My heart felt like lead and, with all might, I had to pull it through the shabby blue door. Philippe was driving, holding my hand, while I was lolling in my seat, dreaming of him and dreading the time when he had to leave. We felt so good together, a perfect fit, like two pieces of a puzzle.

We swapped places. I drove across the mountains, gripping his hand and wondering how I would survive the next two weeks without his touch, how I had been able to live without him so far.

Philippe leant over, kissed me and murmured: "What will I do without you?"

We arrived at the coast faster than I had wished for, and although I had slowed down considerably long ago I could not deny the fact that the journey was coming to an end and separation neared. We swapped places again and a last kiss.

We arrived in Taghazout. Philippe stopped by the side of the road.

"Kate, *chérie*, you need to buy a mobile phone, but while I can't contact you I will phone Lahcen with messages for you. Does that sound alright?"

I nodded.

"*A bientôt, ma belle.*" Philippe hugged me. "Only two weeks. Don't forget me. *Je t'adore.*"

"Take care."

Miserably I watched him drive off.

"Come, eat with me, and we can talk." Yassin had appeared from nowhere.

"I can't, Yassin, I would be sitting on your terrace weeping like an old woman. Not the best advertisement for your restaurant!" I shot past him and fled to the beach.

I sat down on my favourite rock and threw stones into the sea as I always did in tricky situations. I felt strangely empty. I did not feel like going up to Taliouine. Not even my house interested me. Everything had changed. I had to re-organise my life.

"If you are not happy, you have to talk to a friend." Yassin put a bucket of fish down on the sand and weighed a sharp knife in his hand. "Where have you been? With a nearly married man?"

"He is not a nearly married man, Yassin. I am sure you know that. We went to Marrakech for two days. And yes, thank you, I had a great time."

"So why are you unhappy?"

I turned to him. "Because he has gone. To France."

"He is not coming back?" Yassin looked up.

"Of course he is coming back! But only in two weeks."

"In two weeks?" he laughed, almost hysterically. "Two weeks is no time, you will see. You have much, much work to do. Everybody was asking for you. They were all worried. I said not to worry, but I said no more."

I weighed a pebble in my hand. "You are a good friend, Yassin. I am sorry, we didn't have a good time lately," I said softly.

"Don't worry, sometimes you have good times, sometimes you don't. We will survive." He examined the edge of his knife, which glinted in sun. "You like him?"

I had to throw three stones before I was able to answer.

"I am in love with him, Yassin."

"Is he in love with you?"

I sighed. "Yes, I think so. Looks like it."

"So, very good. You like him, he likes you. He is a good man. He will be back in two weeks. You must build your house

251

now. People are waiting for you. They want to work, they need money. When you work time goes quicker."

My friend Yassin was as always spot on. I jumped up. My mind was suddenly filled with energy. My confused thoughts had been shaken back into their place by Yassin's practical approach.

"Thanks, my friend. I will go up to Taliouine straight away."

He shook his head and took a fish out of the bucket. When I reached the first houses, I turned back to wave. Yassin had not moved. Fish and knife in his hands, he was staring out to sea.

Chapter Thirty-Two

Not a wisp of wind stirred the branches of the Argan trees. The village was dozing in the midday sun. No one was about, except for Raza, the pregnant village dog, who had squeezed herself against a stonewall to find shelter from the sun. She lifted her head, yawned unexcitedly and flopped back onto the sand.

I might be able to slip into my house unnoticed, and then I could pretend I had been inside all weekend. I tiptoed up the path.

With a squeak, Cherifa's door opened and released Nadah, who whirled across the path and threw her arms around me.

"*Madame!*" she shouted, announcing my return with a voice that easily travelled to the rest of the hill top villages. One after the other, the doors opened, producing a colourful spectrum of women holding dishcloths, brushes, knifes and other utensils. They had torn themselves away from whatever they had been doing to offer me a warm welcome.

"*Madame, la bes!*" The Cherifas, Minas and Yasminas seemed pleased. They smiled, took my hand and enveloped me in vast coriander scented hugs.

I was glad that nobody was able to ask me about the weekend.

The women cleared away like summer rain, leaving Nadah hovering by my side, nudging me for more details. I was wavering between being embarrassed and the urge to tell her about it. I wanted her to repeat Philippe's words, to tell me that he had not been lying and that they were not in love. I wanted to know if I could trust him. But there was no language to confide in Nadah. So we ambled along, arm in arm, towards my house. Nadah was humming, while I was lost in thoughts.

Finally she skipped off towards Yasmina's, leaving me as sudden as she had appeared.

My neighbour Yassin strolled along, cleaning his teeth with a splinter. He smiled.

"*Ca va, Madame?*"

"*Oui, merci, Yassin, et toi?*"

His smile widened. I felt uncomfortable.

"What is it, Yassin?"

He threw the toothpick on the floor and fingered in his shirt pocket for his cigarettes.

"*Madame…*" he pointed at his eyes, then at me. He waved his hand vaguely towards Agadir, or Marrakesh, and winked.

My God, he knows. He saw me leave. With the man who was supposed to marry his sister and bring wealth to the rest of the family.

"Yassin, I…" I wondered what to say and blushed.

"*Madame…*" He pulled his finger along his smiling lips as if shutting a zip. With a thumbs-up-sign, he turned and set off in search of a leisurely post-lunch occupation such as a sleep in the shadows.

I laughed nervously and unlocked my house. Bilal and Hamza entered after me, armed with trowel and mortarboard.

Everything was back to normal.

In the night, I woke up with a start.

"Philippe?" I asked into the mute darkness.

It had only been a dream.

I could smell orange blossom and jasmine, the cold odour of mud walls in the night. I saw a beautiful courtyard, lit up by hidden lights. I felt my hand in Philippe's, while sipping the refreshing mint tea he had prepared after arriving back at the house. The chatter in the medina had slowly died down; wooden shutters were closed with metallic thumps. Marrakesh had gone to sleep, except for Philippe and me, who were talking, with the gentle tinkle of the fountain like music playing in the background. We spent hours on the cushions in the corner. I spoke about the building, the problems, the people, and the electrician. It was so good to talk. Philippe stroked my hand and listened. He told me about his trekking business, his plans, his life back in France. The mosque called for prayer. The sun was rising when we finally went to sleep.

He would not be able to phone me. Why did I never buy a mobile phone? I was such a backward person. Did Philippe give me his number? Wondering if he did and why on earth I could not remember, I fell asleep again, hugging my pillow.

During the following week, I finally managed to proceed with the purchase of Cherifa's piece of land. So far, I was still tolerated in the country. Cherifa and I drove to Tamraght and returned to Monsieur Abderrahim's office.

"Your money is in my house, for safety," Monsieur Abderrahim finally said, getting up. "Please wait, while I get it."

We waited, until he returned one hour later. Either, he lived in Agadir and had walked there and back, or he had had lunch and a little nap, while we were sitting in his office: Cherifa and I cooped up in a nutshell filled with a sickly scent of incense sticks and mountain spells, which usually surrounded her.

Monsieur Abderrahim was now dealing with three contracts of mine, including translations.

"Will it take much longer?" I asked.

"Everything will be ready in ten days, *insha'allah*."

"*Souk?*" asked Cherifa, when we were back in the street.

"Of course," I answered. "*Eyeh!*"

A spot of retail therapy would do us good.

Hours later Cherifa and I heaved our purchases into the van and returned to Taliouine. Nadah searched Cherifa's bulging bags, until she found an orange. Giggling, she pressed it into my hand.

"*Madame!*"

In the afternoon, Taliouine was hot and sunny, yet there were clouds below: a cover which was thickening increasingly, looking already like a comfortable winter duvet.

My neighbour Yassin and I were working on the top terrace, dabbing cement here and there, when I saw a wall of fog rushing towards us, dark and thick as smoke. Like a stream of lava, it was rolling down hillsides, across fields, rapidly eating up everything in the way: houses, trees and bushes.

"Yassin, *shuf*!" I said, gripping the terrace wall.

The world was going to end.

Yassin stopped his work and stared, equally aghast, at the spectacle, which was unfolding in front of us. He muttered something and dropped the trowel. As the blanket of fog drew nearer, a strong and exceptionally cold wind blew us nearly off the terrace and brought with it a lot of dust. Instinctively we ducked down to shelter. The fog swallowed up my house, Yassin and me. I was being suffocated by a gigantic duvet. Shreds of fog flurried past. The cold wind pulled my hair, my shirt was flapping. My eyes were sore with sand.

The world re-appeared after a moment, only to be overrun by a second wave.

This time the fog lingered, the sun had gone and it had turned very cold. Quietly, we gathered our tools and retreated to our dwellings.

Having faced such a display of nature's power, I suddenly felt exposed and vulnerable.

I found that I could not sleep any longer. I thought of Philippe, nodded off for half an hour, jerked up, dreamed of Philippe, slept for ten minutes. Doubts were starting to creep into my fond thoughts. Will he really come back? And if he does, what will he say?

"We had a nice time, *ma belle*, but that was then."

Or

"Let's just stay friends."

Or

"While in France I had time to think…"

I tossed and turned in the hostility of the dark night, forbidding myself to think of Philippe ever again in order to get some sleep.

Two days later Bilal could not pretend any longer that there was *beaucoup de travail* left. Every centimetre of the house was covered with a smooth layer of cement, inside as well as outside. Not an inch had escaped his trowel.

Bilal was standing by the kitchen shelf, mortarboard in his hand. "*Wacha, Madame.*"

Deadline day had arrived. I was happy with the work he had done and regretted not being able to give him more work.

"Bilal *travailler*. Essaouira." Moulham, who had entered the house, explained.

Bilal looked pleased and lifted four fingers.

"*Pour quatre semaines*," Moulham translated.

I was glad. A job for four weeks was better than nothing.

Chapter Thirty-Three

Yassin and Digby were busy because now I had acquired the pathway I needed help to lay down the concrete.

At first, I had thought of creating a garden, a beautiful green shady oasis, maybe a modest copy of what I had seen in Marrakech, until I realised that it was a tad too ambitious; I had neither water nor soil to feed my garden. All that would grow on the sandy and rocky ground were cactus plants and some of their rubber-leaved relatives. Nothing colourful. I could overcome these problems by buying a lorry-load of soil, heaping it onto my rocks and crisscross it with pipes to provide a constant dribble of water. It seemed obscenely wasteful to me, when my neighbours could not afford to fill up their cisterns for even their basic needs like washing and drinking.

What would happen to my garden when I left and only returned months later? With the water supply cut, my colourful oasis would most probably turn into a display of papery brownish has-beens, a cemetery, a battlefield, where no one survived, to which I would return one day feeling like a murderer.

No, it was wiser to create a yard, and grow whatever I wanted in pots, which I could take with me or give away. Lacking more exotic seeds, I rummaged through my supply of

259

pulses and sowed lentils, beans and peas in cut-off water bottles to start a modest copy of Majorelle Gardens in Marrakesh.

The first thing we needed was a great amount of rocks, to bring the path up to the level of the house and *le parking*. My neighbours were full of ideas how to help and at the same time make some dirham out of my need.

Moulham offered me a pile of rocks from the back of his field.

"Two *litros*." He held up two fingers.

I laughed about his persistence and offered him the equivalent in dirham. He shrugged his shoulders and walked off.

Yasmina offered me what seemed to be the back wall of her kitchen for twenty dirham.

"*Ariul!*" Yassin-my-neighbour pulled my sleeve and pointed at his bony donkey which was chewing on a piece of cardboard.

"*Shokran*, Yassin, that is really kind." I was touched by his helpful offer. It would save me a lot of money. I could take the donkey up the hillside and fill the wicker baskets with as many stones as we needed.

Yassin searched his pockets until he found a crumbled fifty-dirham note. He held it under my nose and beamed at me.

Nothing was free in this village.

After an arduous discussion with nobody to translate Yassin-my-neighbour, Digby and I agreed to start by using the rocks from Yasmina's kitchen wall. The following day Yassin would take the donkey and collect stones on the hillsides, for which I would pay him.

I gave Yasmina twenty dirham and explained to her that we would come and take the rocks.

"*Ghasad!*" Tomorrow.

Yasmina swept, hummed and nodded.

Yassin-my-neighbour appeared by my side. He watched his sister and shook his head. Then he turned his attention on to me. "*Madame –Mina fait le tajine*," he invited me for the evening.

I unearthed potatoes and vegetable from the depth of my van and thrust them into Yassin's arms, so Mina could add them to the stew.

I pottered around my building site until after sunset. Then I dragged a sack of cement over to Yassin and Mina's dwelling. Yassin's face lit up at the sight of my offering.

"*Shokran, Madame.*" He yanked the sack into the tiny yard.

"You need a proper roof, Yassin," I said, pointing at the ceiling.

Yassin grinned. The last rain had washed the plastic sheet of his lean-to away and forced Yassin, Mina and little Jalal to sleep in the old stone dwelling again.

I was woken up by a noise, which I had not heard for a long time. It was the shrill and relentless whistling of the Chergui, the hot dry wind from the desert. I tried to open my eyes but they were already sore and as rough as sandpaper. I felt my way to the kitchen and groped for the breakfast utensils. With a groan, I sank down at the table to devour my bread. It had a gritty feel to it and I ate a banana instead. I was getting a headache.

Soon things started to go wrong.

Gingerly I stepped out of my van and shrunk straight back, feeling as if I was being attacked by an army of hairdryers.

"*Madame, Madame.*" Yassin was unusually agitated and waved me to follow him.

Together we looked at his donkey. It was a pitiful sight. The donkey had cut its hoof and was bleeding heavily. Mina was administering a greenish gooey paste to the wound. She looked up shortly and nodded at me. There was no way we could use the donkey to collect stones.

Yassin was crushed by the injury. The donkey was very important for the villagers, and not everyone was able to afford to buy and keep one. How would the family get water from the well now?

Yasmina opened the door, looked left and right and, on seeing me, pulled the door shut behind her and came running.

"*Madame, Madame,*" she screamed in a similar pitch as the whistling Chergui, waving her broom about. She came to a sudden stop in front of me, panting. Blisters of sweat covered her face.

"*Madame, cent dirham.*" Yasmina grinned and rested her broom on the ground like a spear.

I sighed. We haggled for about five minutes more or less seriously and parted with the agreement that the stones of the wall would cost me another fifty dirham. I handed over the money. She hid it in the folds of her dress and skipped away, humming and singing as usual.

It was a mad price to pay for a pile of stones, when they were lying around in abundance everywhere outside the village. Only, how would I get them to the house without a donkey?

I paid Moulham a visit. He had sorted through his heap of rocks and for the same price there were now only small ones for me to take. I felt cheated and angry, but soon realised that it was Melikha, who did not want the larger rocks sold. I did not blame her. When her husband was finally ready to build a house she would probably be the one who had to collect the building materials.

When Yassin and Digby started to take down Yasmina's wall, she tried to stop them.

I could not follow the heated conversation, but from Yasmina's mention of dirham and marking the middle of the wall with her hand I assumed that she was only going to give me half of it for the seventy dirham I had paid.

Yassin-my-neighbour came over to explain that she was worried all the other walls might collapse if the kitchen wall was being dismantled. This would mean that she might have to rebuild her whole dwelling, which would of course be more costly for me. And that anything under two hundred dirham was therefore completely unacceptable to her.

I shook my head. Her dwelling, built from solid breezeblocks, would not move an inch if we took away the stones. It probably would not even twitch during an earthquake.

What happened then, I could only blame on the wind. My friend Yassin used to say that the Chergui does strange things to people, that it plays hide and seek with their sanity, that the hot blow of its breath kindles a fire inside people's head.

Yasmina went berserk. She gave a perfect imitation of Ali the electrician. She shouted, her shrill voice cutting through the hot dry presence of the wind and travelling across the village, the hillside, and possibly half of Morocco. She lifted up stones and started hurling them at us.

When a stone hit Digby, he swore and fled into the house. Yassin and I followed, slammed the door shut and listened to the dull thuds of stones hitting the wall of my house. I sank down on the floor and waited for Yasmina to cool down, while Digby and Yassin tapped their foreheads and whispered together.

Who needed neighbours like her? I have tried to see a positive side to her despite her annoying habits: the constant humming and sweeping, her weird animal talk with dogs and cats. Sitting on the floor of my house listening to Yasmina competing with the wind in pitch and persistence, I felt my optimism being blown away.

Not only Yasmina, but also Cherifa had turned against me, She had started to complain about the stonewall, which Moulham was building outside my front door for six hundred dirham. How could I have ever agreed to this price? I did not even need the wall. Moulham had been asking me for a job, and everybody seemed so poor that I agreed. The wall defied Moulham's expertise, and I had to show him several times how to put up a string level, which did not follow the slope of the street. Cherifa was objecting to the wall for reasons unknown to me, possibly punishment for employing her arch enemy.

What a day! I felt short-fused and sick. Maybe the wind was getting to me, too. Maybe I had finally caught the gastric flu which had struck every single person in the village. Except for myself. So far.

The following day I was sick. I had been throwing up all night. My stomach had gone into a tight double knot. I was lying on my bed curled up like a woodlouse, trying to think of nothing. Nobody was working as it had been raining heavily all night. Raindrops were drumming onto the roof of the van forming a curtain of miniature waterfalls on the windows. It was cold, and I toyed with the idea of lighting the gas heater, but then decided against it as it was April and not November, and I was in Morocco and not England.

Unwell and depressed, I did nothing else but move from bed to toilet and from toilet to bed all day. I felt lonely. Philippe crept back into my thoughts. I had not heard anything from him. Then again, I had not seen Lahcen either who was supposed to be the messenger.

Luckily, I had no phone, I comforted myself, or I would stare at its silent presence all the time imploring it to ring. I was quite sure by now that Philippe had given me his mobile number, even the telephone number where he was staying in France. I must have lost the piece of paper. How could that have happened? I suspected I had done it on purpose, in case I would phone Philippe and find he could not even remember who I was.

"Kate? Kate who?"

"Of course. Kate. Kate from Taliouine. And how are you these days?"

"Pardon? No, I will not be coming back for a while. Unforeseen difficulties in the company, you know."

"Good luck with your house then and I'll see you around, okay?"

I engaged myself in a fantasy about the *Continent* supermarket in Las Palmones in the south of Spain, right near the ferry port. One day of driving and I could be there, buying lots of useless but comforting European goods.

I was still not better the next day, neither was the weather. I watched the rain running down my window. The pathways had turned into torrents. The village looked bleak and different. It was grey, poor and dirty. It probably was on a sunny day too, but it was easier to romanticise these features when the sky was blue and the sun caressed my warmth-starved body. I stared out of the

264

window and decided that at that moment Taliouine was the least attractive place I had been to in my life.

Once again, I felt overwhelmed by the task I had set myself. Although the shell was finished, my house was still far from being habitable. There was a mountain of work to do, people to find, materials to choose, language to learn, neighbours to pacify, disappointments to take.

I was ashamed to admit that I had started to dream of a partner, preferably a nice husband, a patient Berber speaking DIY-man, who was good with people and who could take over for a while. What had happened to the old me, the woman who used to smile and say 'thank you' to every new obstacle in her path because she enjoyed the extra challenge?

I had also started dreaming about going back to England, which I was no less ashamed to admit, as it was the ultimate defeat.

After three days, the rain stopped, as had the frequency of my visits to the toilet. I was physically better, but my body was exhausted and drained. My spirits had not lifted yet, not even when I was told that the prolongation of my visa had been granted. Maybe I just needed a change of scene. I could travel somewhere in Morocco, this lovely country, just for a holiday.

Then Moulham and I fell out.

Chapter Thirty-Four

"*Cent dirham, Madame.*" Moulham's eyes were teasing me in their usual playful manner. He had abandoned his little building site in front of my house after twenty minutes of listless loitering, during which he had rearranged his tools, rolled a cigarette and eaten the sandwich I had put out for his lunch.

It was 8. 30 in the morning and he had crept up behind me, while I was inspecting the progress of my yard. He startled me with his demand for more money. I shook my head. I had already given him an advance of three hundred.

"You finish the wall – *et après* - I pay you the remaining three hundred dirham, *wacha*?" I said in my customary village speak.

"*Oui, Madame, wacha.*"

It should not have taken him long, but Moulham was a busy man. He frequently chugged down to Taghazout on his ancient bike in pursuit of business as he called it, which involved a good chat with the fishermen, a *tajine* in the local cafe and the search for an empathetic tourist who was willing to bring him a *litro* back from his excursion to Agadir. Therefore, the finishing of my wall and equally, the payment for his work seemed an event in the distant future. Still, I decided to advance him another fifty dirham.

"I will go to Agadir and bring back *cinquante* dirham," I explained, lifting up five fingers and painting a zero with thumb and index finger.

"*Oui, Madame,*" he said. "*Shokran.*"

I finished the inspection of my yard, which was coming on nicely, made a list of all the things I would need from Agadir and was about to climb inside my van, when Moulham grabbed my arm.

"*Cent dirham, Madame,*" Moulham said slowly. His eyes glinted, and he opened a gunfire of Berber, out of which the word *police* was the only one that struck me as familiar. Familiarity also lay in the setting of the scene, as Ali the electrician had behaved exactly the same way a few weeks ago.

Moulham let go of me and started striding up and down, a pixie on the warpath, slapping his child-sized hands together and telling me that he was finished with me.

"*Safi!*" he shouted, "too much for my head."

"Same for me," I said and drove off, wondering if I was blessed or cursed to have a bunch of dramatists as neighbours.

When I returned from Agadir, I once again did not feel comfortable enough to go up to the village, with Moulham, the village boss now being my enemy, and decided to stay the night on the beach in order to have a chat and a drink with my new-age-traveller friends and find safety in numbers.

Two weeks had nearly gone by, and there was neither a sign of Philippe, nor had I seen Lahcen.

"Told you so," whispered a voice inside me.

"Shut up," I said, tempted to rush to Ait Tabbia to visit Lahcen.

I did not go. Hearing that Philippe had not phoned with a message for me would probably push me over the edge of the crumbling cliff my live resembled now.

The probably more likely possibility that Philippe had indeed phoned for me did not cross my mind. My self-esteem had been destroyed by Tobin years ago.

I spent nearly all of the next day on the beach to clear my head. Long walks along the sea finally lifted my spirits. The tide was out, and small waves rolled in from miles away; the foamy water lapped about my feet. I walked far out, away from everybody. The wet ochre coloured sand was giving way under my steps and then enveloped my feet in cool soft hugs. It was wonderful. The occasional boulder was nestling in the sand, maybe once upon a time thrown down from the hills by giants. When the water rushed out, puddles remained which were inhabited by prawns. They were transparent, fragile and difficult to spot, as if made from glass. Just like me.

After I had spent the day in pure indulgence and thereby drawn strength from the powerful ocean I felt better. The fogginess in my head had cleared. I decided to take Moulham his remaining three hundred dirham and ask him to stop working on the wall. He would have to leave it as it was. Cherifa was against it anyway, because - as I had managed to find out - there was not enough room for the water lorry to get past without going over her precious *farine*. I guessed that as soon as I left to go back to Spain for a new visa my neighbours would take it down and use the stones to rebuild Yasmina's kitchen wall.

Back in Taliouine, I handed the money over to Moulham and told him to stop working, only to find that he considered the wall finished anyway. We shook hands, but we were not friends anymore, not for the time being. I felt hurt, exploited wherever I turned.

Yassin and Digby had managed to get enough stones together to bring the path up to the right level. They must have collected them while I was sick. Soon after, they had laid down the concrete. I was grateful to Digby, who still succeeded in making my neighbour Yassin work reliably and consistently, probably by threatening to tell Cherifa should he lapse.

The last thing for the two men to do was to build two pillars for the gate, which was going to enclose my little yard.

Two days of heavy rain followed. After taking my van down to Taghazout, I could not get back up the hill to *le parking*. The track had been softened and partially washed away. I had no choice but to keep going past Cherifa's house and Abdul-the-epicerie-man's house and park on the village square in front of the school.

It was a nightmare. My van sat in the square like something left behind after an extraterrestrial invasion. The children whooped and surrounded me, calling for sweets and money. They banged their little fists angrily on the side of the van when none of the demanded goodies made an appearance.

"Madame! Madame!" they roared as if I was deaf. *"Bonbon! Dirham! Stylo!"*

The first-rain-since-three-hundred-years-period was not over yet. The showers were heavy, the wind was cold and the highest day temperature was thirteen degrees Celsius. On April 10th! It was warmer in England.

I had noticed the voice inside me, saying, quietly first, then louder: "Brick the house up and leave." After ignoring it for a while, I gave in to it.

Should I brick the house up and leave?

Or should I buy windows, put them in place and then leave? As my new visa would run out anyway within the next two months, it might be safer to brick the house up. Who knows if another prolongation would be granted? Windows would make it too easy to break in, even if they had metal bars and shutters. Very likely, somebody would squat in the house during my absence.

Was I really ready to leave? Had I given up? On myself? On Philippe? Did I not trust him? The answer was I wanted to run away. I had been a master of oppressing and putting on a brave face, but I noticed I was crumbling. Rationally I knew that I had no evidence of Philippe not returning to me. But I was too damaged by years of abuse and betrayal to be confident in a new relationship. I needed to protect myself. Before Philippe could dump me, I had better dump him.

Trouble over the wall in front of my door swelled up again. Lorries with building materials for a house further up the hill came up the track. As the surface of dried mud had been washed away, the drivers used the stone floor of Cherifa's *farine* to get a grip and propel their lorries up the hill.

I watched her through my window striding up and down in front of a considerable audience. The vigorous shaking, swinging and slapping of her hands translated the language I could not understand. With a shrill voice, she was blaming the lorries' difficulties on my new wall. She worked herself up into a fury. With extraordinary strength, she rolled a rock from the field onto her *farine* and blocked it.

I withdrew from the window and busied myself with sorting out my tools, screws and nails, but I could not avoid listening to the heated discussion of the villagers who had gathered outside. They were probably discussing my monetary contribution to compensate for the difficulties my wall was causing. Maybe for six thousand dirham Cherifa would remove the rock on the *farine*. Or, maybe for nine hundred dirham Yassin would let Mina take the wall down again. Maybe for one hundred *litros* of wine Moulham would do it himself.

Something snapped inside me.

I tore the front door open with the might of someone who had blown a fuse. It nearly came off its rusty hinges, hit the stonewall with a bang, bounced back and whacked me neatly in the side. Flinching, I stepped outside. Everyone went quiet.

"What is wrong?" I demanded to know in English.

Nobody said anything; some shifted uncomfortably, and eyes were scanning the ground for ways out.

I pointed at the wall. "Take it, Cherifa," I continued in English. "Take it. I don't want it. It is a piece of shit work anyway." Shaking, I went back inside my house.

My neighbours went quietly on their ways.

I stared at my tools, feeling a familiar burning in my throat and an uncomfortable tickle in my nose. Hot and slowly, a couple of tears made their way down my face and landed on a screwdriver.

I was worn out. It was as if day-in and day-out I was dealing with a handful of jealous toddlers about to throw a tantrum.

Brick it up! Brick it up!

I left the deserted village and walked down to Taghazout to find my friend Yassin in his café. I needed him.

He was not there. I shrugged my shoulders.

'Alright!' I silently screamed at his cafe. 'Don't speak to me then.'

In the night, I lay awake, pondering what to do. I did not want to close all the doors behind me by selling the house; however, I needed to get away for a while. If I opted for safety – who was going to brick up the openings for windows and door? Digby had already left and my neighbour Yassin could take anything between two weeks and two years. I wanted it to be done by yesterday.

All of a sudden, I was in a hurry to get away. I drove to Aourir to find Larbi and ordered what I had calculated I would need: one hundred and fifty breezeblocks, four bags of cement and ten bags of sand, which he would deliver in the afternoon.

I spent midday on the beach. When I wanted to leave, I found to my surprise that I was not allowed back onto the main road. It was blocked for a modest procession of King Mohamed and his newly wedded wife. Because of the ongoing in Palestine they had deemed it impropriate to have the customary grand royal wedding celebration and just went for a pleasurable drive up the coast. The people loved them for this, and so did I. Nine helicopters were skimming the area. I felt abandoned and lonely.

The next morning, after having parked in the field on the edge of Taliouine again, as I used to when I did not have *le parking*, I mused over what to do. I urgently needed to find a bricklayer.

I was about to settle into the comforting hug of self-pity, when two heads appeared outside my window: Yassin-the-bricklayer and Mohamed, his cousin. Before they could knock on the door, I shot out of the van to welcome them like long lost children. Allah must be wanting to get rid of me to answer my prayers without *insha'allah* and delay!

"Yassin! Mohamed!" I cried, nearly tripping over on the way out of my van. "How did you know?"

Of course, they had no idea of my desperation and shrunk back, as if afraid I might embarrass them by giving them a great big hug.

"*Madame, travail?*" Yassin-the-bricklayer asked.

"Are you not working for the builder anymore?" I sign-languaged.

Yassin-the-bricklayer and Mohamed shook their heads.

"*Azih!* No time to lose." I locked my van and ran ahead to my house. The two young men followed at a safe distance, cautiously, as if I had gone completely mad since they had seen me last. When we finally gathered in what was going to be the kitchen I explained what needed to be done. The window openings and the terrace door had to be bricked up. A wall had to be built to enclose the yard and a few bricks laid here and there to stop intruders from entering via the walls.

Yassin-the-bricklayer and Mohamed went to work straight away. I stepped outside.

The village people started to walk past. Their faces were screwed up to question marks, their dark eyes fixed on mine, wondering what was going on and why I was employing people who were not from Taliouine.

The only one who understood was my neighbour Yassin. He was *tranquil* about it as usual and smiled his all-understanding, lazy smile.

"*C'est bien, Madame.*" He patted my back and sat down at the edge of the field. Leaning back against a rock, he lit a cigarette.

The air was still. A smell of wood fire lingered in the dusty alleyways. I inhaled deeply imagining the women preparing the dough for the first bread of the day. There was peacefulness about Taliouine, which I had not felt for a long time. Many of the village people had gathered near the house and, for once, were not quarrelling. The village dogs were dozing nearby. The work was going ahead without complications and the sun was warm on my back – just when I was getting ready to leave.

I knew by then that it was not going to last. I had learnt that Taliouine was not at all the restful place it appeared to be.

Moulham arrived on the scene. His designer-labelled cap was threatening to slide off his head. His eyes were blinking furiously. He strode into my house. I followed him.

"Ma bêche!" he shouted.

"I don't have your spade," I said, "as you can see for yourself." With a gesture, I invited him to look around.

It made him only angrier."You give to Yassin," he shouted, jabbing a finger in my direction and with this, he marched out of the house to trouble his nephew, who was still enjoying his cigarette in the sunshine.

Yassin, my good-natured neighbour, lost his temper. I remembered the only time I had witnessed it before: pictures of Yassin shoving a raging Ali out of the village popped up in front of my eyes.

Yassin jumped up, threw his cigarette in front of the old man's feet and went to his house. Within seconds, he was back with his own spade. He smashed it onto the boulders of the *farine*. The wood splintered and the shovel flew across the field. It was a very aggressive act for a man, who detested violence. I felt sorry for him. Yassin was driven by oppressed anger and resentment against Moulham, which sometimes had to be vented. I did not understand the meaning of the words he spat at his uncle, but I was glad not to be on the receiving end.

The pack of dogs, usually brazen and fearless, got up and moved to the other end of the field, ears and tails drooping.

After Moulham had marched off towards Taghazout, there were no more disturbances.

With every brick put in place, the light faded more from my little house. It was like a door slowly closing on me. The air started to grow cool inside, and a smell of damp cellars rose from the shadowy corners. A cockroach rushed up the wall.

At six o'clock Yassin-the-bricklayer put his trowel down. The house was dark. Every opening had been bricked up. I felt like being buried alive and quickly ushered the two men out through the front door into the pre-sunset tranquillity of the village. I locked the metal door.

The village people had realised by now what I was doing. I looked at them briefly. Nadah fiddled with her belt and examined her shoe, turning her foot this way and then that way. Nashiema smiled weakly, holding Samir's hand. Melikha was hugging her large baby, her eyes boring into mine above its bald head. Wherever I looked, I noticed stunned and curious expressions. Only Cherifa was smirking, her eyes shining like black marbles.

Just like a witch, I thought, feeling for the keys in my pocket.

Nobody could believe that I was suddenly leaving. Neither could I. Nor could I speak about it to anyone.

I hugged Nashiema, fragile as a butterfly in my arms, and gave little Samir a kiss. Nadah pulled me to her ample chest and pressed me into the softness of her body. She smelled of mint tea, bread, laughter and shoe swapping. Neither of the twins said a word. Nadah clung to me, firmly clasping my hand. It was surprisingly difficult to leave, even more so when it was time to say good-bye to my neighbour Yassin and his wife Mina. Yassin promised to look after the house. With her small brush made from twigs, Mina swept furiously the path in front of my house, as if to make things better and persuade me to stay. When she lifted her head, I saw tears rolling down her face.

I gently freed my hand from Nadah's grip.

Down in Taghazout I invited the two bricklayers to a *tajine* in their favourite café, said good-bye to one or two friends who happened to be around and spent a last night on the beach. I was amazed, how quickly I had managed to get away and close this chapter. I was bursting with adrenalin, which stopped my brain from thinking about consequences.

I did not dare look for Yassin, my best friend. My former best friend.

DOWN TOWARDS THE SEA

Chapter Thirty Five

Three days later I was in Gibraltar. My van was parked up at
Catalan Bay. Colonies of seagulls were swooping down from the
Rock. The screeching was familiar and comforting. I had not
heard it for months. I was surrounded by roast chicken, salad,
granary bread, Branston pickle and a good cup of tea. A bottle of
wine stood waiting in the fridge. The van was covered with
pages of *The Times* and *The Telegraph*. Just as I had dreamt
during those dreary rainy days in Taliouine.

And I had finally acquired a mobile phone.

I was reading but not taking in a single word. More often, I
found myself staring across the Strait towards Morocco. Images
started to pop up. My mind always returned to Mina with tears
rolling down her face, and to Nadah and Nashiema's stunned
expressions, Nadah holding my hand.

Finally, I could no longer avoid thinking of Philippe. The
memory of our days in Marrakech hit me with full force.
Searching for a tissue I stumbled across my orange pinkish dress,
which I had never washed because it smelled of Marrakesh and
Philippe, and which I had hidden in a cupboard because it made
me cry.

As I was crying anyway I pulled it out and buried my face
in it. After a while, I noticed something in the pocket. It was a

277

piece of paper. I pulled it out and straightened it. It contained the faded remains of numbers. Philippe's telephone numbers.

Without thinking about it, I sent the newspapers flying to the floor to unearth my new phone and punched in one of the numbers. My hands were shaking so much that I dropped the phone twice before I managed to dial.

"*Oui*?"

His voice was warm and familiar. I felt as if I was slowly immersing myself into a hot bath. I cleared my throat.

"Philippe…"

"Kate! Where are you? Are you ok? What is going on? I was so worried."

"In Gibraltar," I sniffed, but I was relieved. No "Kate who?", like in my worst nightmares.

"Where are you?" I asked.

"In Taghazout. I arrived back two days ago," he said.

I fiddled with my tissue.

"I will come and get you," he continued.

He must have driven thousands of miles to get back to Taghazout, and he was prepared to drive another thousand just to see me in Gibraltar.

"Kate? Please, don't hang up," he said.

With one hand, I wrestled a piece of bread out of the bag.

"I missed you." he added quietly.

I looked at my watch. If I hurried I could take the next ferry across.

"Kate, are you still there?"

But he never phoned me, when he was away, did he? Or did Lahcen just not tell me? Did he forget to pass on a message?

I could be back in Taghazout in two days, if I left now, I thought, tossing the slice of bread around. I was not hungry.

What stopped me from heading straight to the ferry port was that I wasn't sure if I really wanted to go back. Nothing would have changed in Taliouine, and I did not feel like returning to the same chaos. Not even with the prospect of seeing Philippe again. Maybe it was time for me to return to London, to find a job, a place to live. I just had to manage somehow. I have had a few years off, have tried and seen a lot of things – more than other people had. That should last me for the rest of my life.

"Kate?"

The truth was that I did not want to spend the second half of my life dreaming about the past and a voyage I had once embarked on. Morocco was meant to be the end of a journey and the beginning of a new life, not London. London signified past, and the past had not been very kind to me. I was not ready yet to admit defeat.

"Kate, talk to me."

"Things have been difficult," I offered lamely.

"I know. I have heard about it."

I poked little holes into the bread. It felt spongy. I pushed it away.

"Let me help you."

Probably nothing like as healthy and tasty as the homemade bread in Taliouine. I leant back and looked out of my window across the water.

"Kate, it was terrible to come back here and find that you had gone. Have you forgotten about us?"

Forgotten about us? I couldn't even begin to explain.

"No, I haven't forgotten about us. It just seemed good to...to get away for a while." I found it rather well put.

"Listen. If you feel like a little holiday - would you like to meet me in Marrakech?"

Sailing boats were bobbing on the waves on their way through the Strait of Gibraltar. I wondered where they were heading. Casablanca? Marrakesh?

"What did you just say?" I sat up.

"I will meet you at the gate, Bab Doukkala, say six o'clock tomorrow? Do you want to meet me? Can you make it?"

My heart started beating faster. My eyes followed the outlines of the Rif Mountains on the African continent, razor sharp against the blue sky. I loved Morocco. And I was in love with Philippe. I had almost forgotten why I had left.

"Should be able to."

"Will I see you tomorrow then? Kate, I can't wait."

"Tomorrow at six. " I switched my phone off and watched the seagulls dance above the waves. "Tomorrow, *insha'allah!*"

The Berbers lived in North Africa long before the arrival of the Arabs, and their culture probably dates back more than 4000 years.

Tachelhit, Tamazight and Tarifit are the main Berber dialects spoken in Morocco.

Translations into English...

Azih!	Come!
Shuf!	Look!
La bes?	Berber greeting
Bejer	Answer to *la bes*
Insha'allah	So God will
Sir! Sir fhalek!	Go away!
Beslama	Good bye
Tajine	Traditional Moroccan stew
Mu'ahd'dhin	Muezzin
Adhan	Prayer
Allah Akbar	God is great
Oho/Eyeh	No/Yes
Mezyan	Good
Rial	Old Moroccan currency
Ghedda	Tomorrow
La, shokran	No, thank you
Wacha	Ok. That's it.
Zig sbah	Today
Eyeh	Yes
Ifulki	Good, beautiful
Shokran	Thank you
Baksheesh	Bribe
Calamar	Calamaris, octopus rings
Assalam aleikum	Hello
Aleikum assalam	Response to *Assalam aleikum*
Kif kif	The same
Litro	Litre bottle of wine
Farine	Flour
Safi	Enough, done
Imiksimik!	Not good at all!
Khaib	Bad
Mekin mushkeel	No problem
Ariul	Donkey
Ghasad	Tomorrow
Cimar	Cement

Dirham	Moroccan currency

French

Eau Potable	Drinking water
Commune maritime	Maritime district
Commune rurale	Rural district
Huile d'Argan	Argan oil
Un jour	One day
Frère	Brother
Mange!	Eat!
Ca va?	Alright?
Je suis desole	I am sorry
Monsieur le Notaire	The notary
…a du retard	…will be late
Entrez!	Come in!
S'il vous plait	Please
Assez-vous	Take a seat
Comment puis-je vous aider?	How can I help ?
Contrat de vente	Contract of purchase
Les voleurs	Thieves
Une baguette? Deux? Trois?	One baguette? Two? Three?
Au revoir	Good bye
Excusez-moi	Excuse me
Regarde!	Look!
Attendez!	Wait!
Combien?	How much?
Un cadeau	A present
Fils	Son
Travail	Work
D'accord?	Okay?
Choisir	To choose
Mariage	Marriage
Demain	Tomorrow
Ami	Friend

Bonne nuit	Good night
Bonbon	Sweets
Voulez-vous achetez?	Do you want to buy?
Le parking	Parking spot
Après	After, later
Pour l'essence	For the petrol
Pour faire le course	For the shopping
Les timbres	Stamps
Combien?	How many?
Dix huit	Eighteen
Tu veux travailler?	Do you want to work?
Murs	Wall
Bric	Breezeblocks
Ici	Here
Comme ca	Like this
Pas de problème	No problem
Beaucoup de travaux	A lot of work
C'est bien	Ok
Pas cher	Not expensive
Camion	Lorry
Tu compris?	Do you understand?
Bon prix	Good price
A la prochaine	Until next time, see you later
Fini	Finished
Attendez!	Wait!
De rien	Not for that, no problem
Peut-être	Maybe
Cent	One hundred
Ce n'est pas fini	It is not finished
C'est bon pour ventilation	Good for ventilation
L'argent	Money
Midi	Midday
Fermer	Closed
Arrêtez!	Stop!
La maison	House

Très jolie	Very pretty
Je voudrais parler avec...	I would like to talk to...
Parlez-vous français ?	Do you speak French?
La femme	Woman, wife
Donnez-moi l'argent!	Give me money!
Monsieur le directeur	The manager, director
Cherchez!	Search!
Mangez!	Eat!
L'électricien	Electrician
Il habite a...	He lives in...
Randonnes	Walks, hikes
De rien	Not for that
Encore	Again
Trois mille	Three thousand
Cinq cent	Five hundred
Beaucoup d'argent	A lot of money
Je t'adore	I like you
A bientôt	See you soon
Cinquante	Fifty
La bêche	Spade

German

Deutsche Kaffeestuben	German Café
Brot	Bread